
AGRICULTURE AND FORESTRY DIVISION

General Editor: J. E. NICHOLS

BEEF PRODUCTION

BEEF PRODUCTION

BY

T. L. DODSWORTH, B.Sc.(Agr.), Ph.D.

Head of the Division of Animal Husbandry,
North of Scotland College of Agriculture

PERGAMON PRESS

OXFORD · NEW YORK · TORONTO
SYDNEY · BRAUNSCHWEIG

Pergamon Press Ltd., Headington Hill Hall, Oxford

Pergamon Press Inc., Maxwell House, Fairview Park, Elmsford, New York 10523

Pergamon of Canada Ltd., 207 Queen's Quay West, Toronto 1

Pergamon Press (Aust.) Pty. Ltd., 19a Boundary Street, Rushcutters Bay, N.S.W. 2011, Australia

Vieweg & Sohn GmbH, Burgplatz 1, Braunschweig

First edition 1972

Library of Congress Catalog Card No. 72-83974

Printed in Great Britain by Watmoughs Limited, Idle, Bradford; and London

08 017017 X (flexicover)

08 017016 1 (hard cover)

CONTENTS

CHAPTER 1

THE PRESENT POSITION AND POSSIBLE DEVELOPMENTS

THERE are many points at which a study of beef production can commence. The method chosen here is first to examine the present position in the United Kingdom and then to speculate upon possible future developments. By using this approach it is possible to indicate the importance of the different aspects or sectors of beef production and lead on to discussion of different systems of production and the need to develop these fully with reference to both technical and economic efficiency.

At one time there was a fairly clear-cut distinction between dairy cattle on the one hand and beef cattle on the other. Dairy cows were used for the production of milk, and prime beef at least was the end product of so-called beef cattle which had been bred out of and suckled by beef cows. This simple distinction, which may well have existed more fully in textbooks rather than in fact on farms, certainly does not apply today. The relative importance in terms of numbers of the National Dairy Herd and of beef cows as sources of animals slaughtered for beef is now well established. About 23% of the animals which are born in and slaughtered in the United Kingdom are cows and bulls most of which are culls from the National Dairy Herd. Cull cows, therefore, make an important contribution to our meat supplies. Of greater importance is the fact that some 55% of the animals which are reared for beef are born and start life in dairy herds. Thus only about 22% of home-born animals which are slaughtered start life in herds which would conventionally be regarded as beef herds. The National Dairy Herd is therefore our most important source of animals for beef production and is followed by beef breeding herds. In addition about 500,000 Irish cattle are imported annually for finishing and slaughter.

The importance of and the possible future development of these sources of animals can be discussed further by referring to national statistics as shown in Table 1.1 which are taken from the *Annual Review and Determination of Guarantees* and the *Annual Abstract of Statistics* (published by HMSO, London). It is recommended that students bring this table up to date each year as the figures are published.

TABLE 1.1
SOME STATISTICS FOR U.K., 1960–9

	1960	1961	1962	1963	1964	1965	1966	1967	1968	1969
Dairy cows ('000)	3165	3245	3290	3247	3144	3186	3162	3214	3226	3275
Beef cows ('000)	848	908	978	1013	982	1018	1106	1141	1152	1211
Cattle imported live for slaughter, excluding calves ('000)	502	685	562	633	700	501	555	641	608	542
Cattle slaughtered ('000)	3010	3336	3397	3545	3361	3188	3355	3585	3526	3380
Calves slaughtered ('000)	860	921	870	703	491	388	508	614	608	418
Beef and veal consumed:										
Imported ('000 tons)	393	401	342	394	329	345	310	316	248	319
Home-produced ('000 tons)	712	758	865	896	903	793	803	852	910	863
% Home-produced	64·4	65·4	71·7	69·5	73·3	69·7	72·1	72·9	78·6	73·0

The amount of beef and veal consumed annually has been fairly constant during recent years, averaging somewhat less than 1,250,000 tons. Of this over 70% is now home produced, less than 30% being imported. The proportion of beef consumed which is home produced has increased over the last 30 years from about 40%, a big increase occurring during the 1950s when the National Dairy Herd was first really exploited as a source of animals for beef production. Before this it was common practice to slaughter dairy bred bull calves at birth, these being regarded as unsuitable for rearing for beef production. The National Dairy Herd has numbered some 3,000,000 to 3,250,000 cows for a considerable period. It, therefore, follows that nearly 1,500,000 calves were slaughtered annually at birth during the late 1940s. These animals, known as bobby or slink calves, yield only a small quantity of meat which must largely be used for manufacturing purposes. This pool of animals was then waiting to be more fully utilised when the demand for an increase in home beef production developed during the early 1950s. "Beef from the Dairy Herd" was a fashionable phrase, and systems were developed for rearing and fattening beef/dairy cross-animals for slaughter first at 2 years and more latterly at 18 months of age. More recently this system of beef production has been endowed with the title of "Semi-intensive" as opposed to the "Intensive" or "All Concentrate" system of production which has only developed since 1961. This latter system also utilises bull calves from the Dairy Herd.

Some measure of the successful development of these systems can be taken from Table 1.1 which shows that the number of calves slaughtered at birth reached a record low level of 388,000 in 1965. This number has since risen again, but some 1,000,000 calves which were formerly slaughtered at birth are now being reared and fattened.

The figures in Table 1.1 also show that the number of "beef cows" has also increased by nearly 43% during the 1960–9 period, thus providing a greater number of beef bred animals for rearing for slaughter.

These developments led to the production of 863,000 tons of beef in the United Kingdom in 1969, this being 73·0% of the total consumed. Home production increased to 910,000 tons in 1968, but this figure, and particularly the proportion of 78·6% home produced, were affected by the ban on importation from the Argentine during an outbreak of foot and mouth disease. These figures for 1968 are therefore abnormal.

The question may now be put: should beef production increase further? Farmers in the United Kingdom are in fact being encouraged to increase the output of home-produced beef in order to reduce the nation's bill for imported food. Some go further and argue that we should not simply look for an increase in beef production but should boldly aim at self-sufficiency. In this context it is interesting to note from Table 1.1 that the mean annual increase over the 1960–9 period was about 15,000 tons and that if this rate of increase is maintained the nation will be self-sufficient by the late 1980s. This assumes an increase neither in the size of the population nor in the level of consumption of beef. This target alone is of considerable magnitude, as the replacement of 300,000 tons of beef now imported would involve the rearing and finishing of an additional 1,200,000 to 1,500,000 animals for slaughter. The achievement of such an increase in production must finally depend upon producers being given a sufficient degree of confidence in price levels and market conditions over a significant period before they or their bankers are prepared to risk the large amount of capital required. It will also depend upon the full utilisation of all animals available now which are suitable for rearing and the production of the additional cattle which would be required. It is, therefore, imperative that all concerned develop fully the technical efficiency of each aspect of beef production. This also becomes necessary even if a target of the magnitude indicated above is reduced and present-day production levels only have to be maintained, but against a background of increasing costs and shrinking profit margins.

The onus is on producers to acquire and put into practice now all the technical information already available. Thus: Can we improve the efficiency of artificial calf-rearing systems? Can we develop further the utilisation of calves now slaughtered at birth? Can we improve the output from hill and upland herds maybe by changing the type of cow used? Can we develop systems of keeping suckler herds on lowground farms profitably to produce more cattle for slaughter? And finally, Can we improve the overall efficiency so that more beef is produced from each animal now slaughtered? The objective of this book is to present some of the available technical information to the farmer and student in the hope that this will assist them to achieve success in these directions.

CHAPTER 2

TYPES OF BEEF AND THE BEEF CARCASE

BEEF is defined in one dictionary as "the flesh of an ox or cow", which may well imply that the compiler appreciated the fact that a big proportion of our beef is obtained from cull cows. The same dictionary tells us that the ox is "a well-known animal that chews the cud, the female of which supplies the chief part of the milk used as human food; the male of the cow especially when castrated". These definitions clearly indicate that beef includes the flesh of a bull and of the castrated bull: steer or bullock, and as no indication is given of age at slaughter this may vary from extremely young to very aged. Beef may therefore vary considerably in type and it seems necessary to give a simple classification of types of beef based on the type of animal and age at slaughter.

The "Bobby calf" or "Slink calf" is slaughtered at less than 2 weeks of age and usually immediately after birth. The proportion of flesh to bone is low and the meat is used for manufacturing purposes.

"Veal" is the flesh of a calf slaughtered at some 6 to 16 weeks of age, having been fed on milk or milk substitute only. The flesh is very pale or even white in colour and is very tender. If the calf is not fit to slaughter for veal at 16 weeks of age, feeds other than milk have to be used. The flesh then becomes darker and does not realise the full veal price when the animal is slaughtered as a "Runner" calf.

"Baby beef", "Beefling" and "Mature beef" are conventional terms used respectively to describe carcases from steers and maiden heifers slaughtered at 15–18, 18–24 and over 24 months of age. The necessity to use these terms is now reduced as a large proportion of our cattle are now slaughtered at less than 2 years of age.

"Cow heifer beef" is obtained from a heifer which has given birth to one calf only. The carcase can be indistinguishable from that of a maiden heifer, especially if the cow heifer is rapidly fattened after calving and is not suckled. It can therefore be argued that cow heifer beef production should be stimulated and the slaughter of maiden heifers discouraged as one method of increasing the output of more calves for beef production.

"Cow beef" is obtained from the carcase of cows which have produced more than one calf, including aged cows. Marked deterioration in carcase quality appears after the third calving and the majority of carcases should be used for manufacturing purposes. The carcase often includes excessive fat and a low proportion of lean meat.

"Bull beef", which should now be classified more correctly as "Mature bull beef", is obtained from the carcase of a culled breeding bull which will usually be 6 or 7 years of age at slaughter. The carcase shows heavy muscular development, particularly in the fore-quarters; the flesh is coarse in texture, dark in colour and is mainly used for manufacturing purposes.

"Barley beef" and "Young bull beef" are deliberately included at the end of this classification because they have only been produced since the early 1960s. The animal is slaughtered at about 12 months of age having received an all-concentrate diet. The flesh is pale in colour, is very tender and the carcases are relatively uniform.

The term "Clean" cattle denotes animals which have not been bred, i.e. steers, maiden heifers and presumably young bulls. A "Rig" is an incompletely castrated animal which shows some development of secondary sexual character such as a heavy crest and fore-quarter.

The terminology used varies in different parts of the country, but the above are all in fairly common usage.

THE BEEF CARCASE

When the animal is slaughtered, it is bled, flayed or skinned, the head, feet and tail are removed, the complete gut is removed, then the heart, lungs and liver are also removed. The remaining carcase is then split down the spine to produce two "sides" of beef. The different products of an animal of 1000 lb. liveweight at slaughter would on average be as follows:

1. Gut contents 140 lb or 14% of the liveweight.

2. Inedible offal, 140 lb or 14% of the liveweight.
3. Edible offal, 140 lb or 14% of the liveweight.
4. Two sides of beef together weighing 580 lb or 58% of the liveweight.

The inedible offal includes the hide, feet, gut casings, lungs, fat trimmings, gall bladder and bladder.

The edible offal consists of the blood, head, stomach, spleen, liver, thick skirt or diaphragm, tail, heart and kidneys.

The farmer receives payment on the weight of the carcase only. This is estimated by the buyer if the animal is sold alive "on the hoof" or is actually measured in the slaughter house when the farmer chooses to sell on a deadweight basis or "on the hook". In the latter case the two sides are weighed immediately after slaughter and while they are still warm, but some weight is lost due to dripping of blood and evaporation of moisture during cooling and the farmer receives payment on the weight of the two sides when cold. This is commonly determined by subtracting 2% from the warm carcase weight. Income from the sale of offal is not returned to the farmer, being used to defray the costs of slaughter. It is said that the butcher "sinks" the offal to pay the costs of slaughter.

In the example given above, the animal of 1000 lb liveweight yielded a carcase weighing 580 lb representing 58% of the liveweight. This percentage yield is referred to as the "Killing out", "Dressing out" or "Dressing" percentage. The dressing percentage increases with increasing degree of fatness which is also referred to as "Finish". It also increases and decreases respectively when the animal is relatively empty or full when weighed before slaughter. Thus if an animal is liberally fed on hay before slaughter the gut will be full, the percentage gut fill will be high at slaughter and the dressing percentage will be low. The producer is then open to the charge of "packing" his animals and butcher buyers will probably avoid bidding for his stock in the sale ring. Conversely, if the animal has to endure a long journey and to stand in a cattle market all day without feed, its gut will be relatively empty when it is weighed on entering the sale ring late in the day. In this case the dressing percentage will be high. Dressing percentage has been used conventionally to measure the value of the live animal, but it must be used with great caution by the novice because it is more grossly affected by gut fill than by degree of fatness. In other words, it is pointless to claim that an animal dressing out at 58% is superior to another dressing out at 55% unless it can be stated that both were weighed at the same time before slaughter and had consumed the same weight and type of feed before slaughter.

CUTTING UP THE SIDE OF BEEF

It is normal practice in many areas to transport the complete side of beef from the slaughter house to the wholesale meat market where it may be sold complete to the retail butcher. Some sides are cut up in the wholesale market to meet the demand by some butchers for varying quantities of individual joints. The side is kept complete as long as possible to minimise loss of weight due to drip and evaporation.

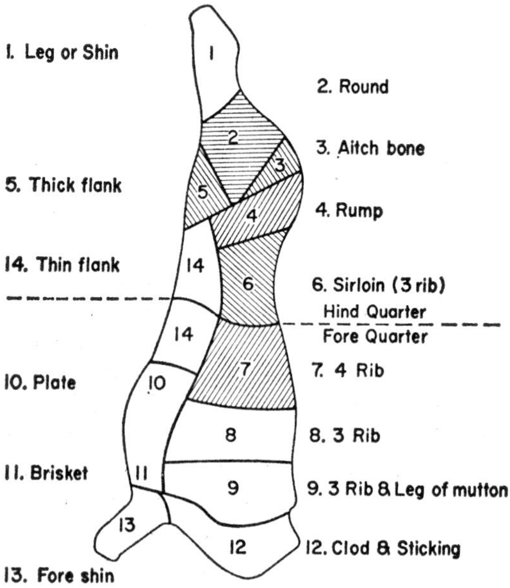

FIG. 2.1. London Smithfield style of cutting.

Two of the many methods of cutting the side of beef into joints are illustrated in Figs. 2.1 and 2.2. The London Smithfield style is shown in Fig. 2.1. From this it will be noticed that the expensive cuts, which are shaded, are found along the back and in the hind-quarter.

Figure 2.2 shows the Scottish Gunbit style of cutting developed to permit the export of the expensive cuts only in one large cut and again reduces shrinkage in transit to a minimum. This style of cutting permits a quick measurement of one aspect of carcase quality, i.e. the percentage of the side weight found in the expensive cuts. Details of some carcases

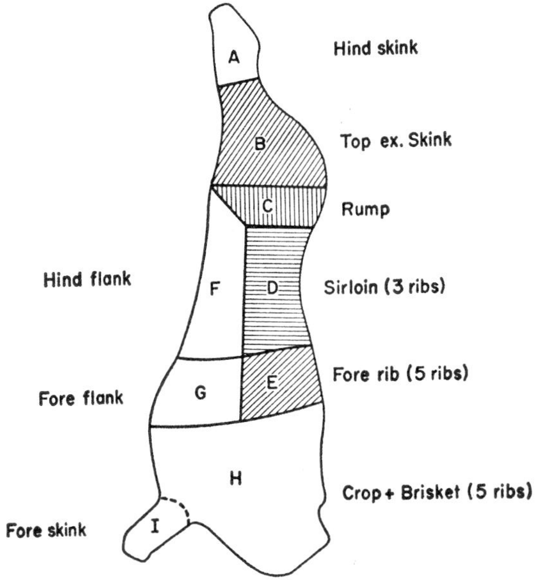

FIG. 2.2. Scottish Gunbit style of cutting.

cut up in this way are given in Table 2.1 to indicate the weight and percentage side weight of each wholesale joint. The data were taken from two lots of beef cross dairy steers which had been fed on the semi-intensive production system which is described later, and are typical of the results obtained when such cattle are slaughtered at some 18 months of age.

TABLE 2.1
CUTTING-UP DATA. STEERS. SEMI-INTENSIVE BEEF

	Charolais × Ayrshire		Beef Shorthorn × Ayrshire	
Side weight (lb)	310·5		275·7	
Kidney fat (lb)	11·2		11·8	
	lb	% side wt	lb	% side wt
Hindquarter (A+B+C+D+F)*	150·6	48·5	136·5	49·5
Forequarter (E+G+H+I)	149·0	48·0	127·6	46·3
Gunbit (A+B+C+D+E)	148·4	47·8	130·7	47·4
Flank (F+G)	41·6	13·4	40·5	14·7
Fore-leg (H+I)	103·9	35·2	93·2	33·8
Roasting (C+D+E)	73·0	23·5	65·9	23·9
Top-piece (A+B)	75·4	24·3	64·8	23·5
Rump (C)	26·7	8·6	23·2	8·4
Sirloin (D)	29·2	9·4	28·1	10·2
Fore-rib (E)	17·1	5·5	14·6	5·3
% composition of side				
Lean	61·8		58·6	
Fat	23·3		27·1	
Bone	14·9		14·3	
Lean : Bone ratio	4·19		4·12	

* See Fig. 2.2.

It should be noted that the expensive cuts constitute less than half of the weight of the side, bone contributes fully 14%, and fat some 20 to 30% of the side weight. No generally acceptable definition of carcase quality has yet been devised, largely due to the fact that carcases are not usually cut into joints until they reach the retail butcher. Measurements of length and depth do not give a reliable estimate of the proportion of the side weight found in the various cuts. Work on this difficult problem is proceeding, but meanwhile the assessment of the quality of a side depends on visual appraisal and the application of a number of subjective points as follows.

The carcase or side should exhibit a full rump and loin and the flesh should extend well down the leg. The ribs should be well covered. There should be a high proportion of meat to bone and of the high-priced cuts. There should be a smooth even covering of fat not more than one-quarter inch deep over the loin and ribs. The fat should be creamy white in colour and the lean should be "marbled" with fat. The carcase should be from a young animal, age being judged in the absence of definite information on the matter by the appearance of the bones. In the carcase from a young animal the cut surfaces of the bone, as seen for example where the spine is split, are suffused with blood and are of fine texture. With advancing age the cut surface becomes pearly white and is coarse in texture.

In the absence of objective measures of carcase quality the butcher must learn through experience how to apply the subjective points given above.

The covering of fat required over the ribs and loin is partly required to minimise shrinkage as already noted. It also prevents undue darkening of the underlying muscle and is of course required for culinary purposes. One-quarter inch is sufficient for these purposes and amply meets the requirements of most consumers. In some markets a greater depth of fat cover is required. The "marbling" fat which is deposited within and between the bundles of fibres in the muscles is of considerable value. During cooking this fat permeates through the lean muscle, improving tenderness and flavour. Results of some dissection work indicate that the most common demand is now for 20–25% of fat in the carcase. Butcher and consumer alike do not want excessive fat which must be trimmed off before the joint is sold. Many farmers do not appear to appreciate fully the significance of this and would benefit from visiting their local abattoir. Examination of carcases is the best indicator of the degree of finish required. This often leads in turn to the marketing of cattle at an earlier stage and the avoidance of wasteful over-fattening which only leads to an increase in food costs and reduction in the profitability of fattening.

FATSTOCK GUARANTEE SCHEME

The minimum price received when fat cattle are marketed by the producer is defined in detail in the Fatstock Guarantee Scheme which is published annually by the Ministry of Agriculture.

Qualifying Standards

General

If presented at a deadweight certification centre, the dressed carcase weight must be not less than 450 lb in the case of a steer and not less than 390 lb in the case of a heifer. The carcase must be of good conformation.

If presented at a liveweight certification centre, the animal must weigh not less than $7\frac{1}{2}$ cwt in the case of a steer and not less than $6\frac{1}{2}$ cwt in the case of a heifer.

Young Liveweight Animals

If presented at a deadweight certification centre the animal must not have cut any permanent incisor teeth and the dressed carcase weight must be not less than 410 lb in the case of a steer and not less than 345 lb in the case of a heifer.

If presented at a liveweight certification centre the animal must not have cut any permanent incisor teeth and must weigh not less than $6\frac{3}{4}$ cwt in the case of a steer and not less than $5\frac{3}{4}$ cwt in the case of a heifer.

Young Bulls

Young bulls will only be accepted for deadweight certification. A young bull carcase must be the product of an animal which has not cut any permanent incisor teeth and must conform to one of the two following standards:

(a) The dressed carcase weight must be not less than 450 lb. The carcase must be of good conformation and the flesh must be moderately firm and the colour must not be dark but may range from a light cherry red to a slightly darker red.

(b) Special young lightweight bulls. The dressed carcase weight must be not less than 410 lb. The carcase must be moderately compact with moderately firm flesh. Colour must not be dark but may range from a light cherry red to a slightly darker red.

There is no upper limit to the weight at which live cattle or carcases may be certified, but the guarantee payment will be restricted to:

	Liveweight	Dressed carcase weight
Steers	13 cwt	830 lb
Heifers	11 cwt	700 lb
Young bulls	Not applicable	830 lb

The guaranteed price for 1971/2 is £12·35 per live cwt. For the purpose of making weekly guarantee payments and to reflect variations in costs and marketing, a seasonal scale of weekly standard prices has been specified which is estimated to be equivalent to the guaranteed price of £12·35 for the year as a whole. Reference should be made to the Fatstock Guarantee Scheme for further details of seasonal variations in prices and such reference is necessary after each annual Price Review.

CHAPTER 3

FACTORS AFFECTING TECHNICAL EFFICIENCY AND PROFITABILITY

THE direct profit made on beef cattle between birth and slaughter is not large. It is therefore sensible that the animal should be retained throughout its life by one owner, thus reducing to a minimum the erosion of profit to the farmer by transport and marketing charges. The point can be illustrated if it is assumed that an animal which is slaughtered at 18 months leaves a gross lifetime profit of £15. The animal may be reared to 6 months of age and then be sold. This involves transport to and from market and a market fee. The process may be repeated at 12 months of age. In such a case at least £5 will have been disbursed by producers from the gross profit of £15 to cover transport costs and market fees before the animal is finally slaughtered. Only £10 remains to be divided among the three producers involved. Clearly the onus is on beef producers to ensure that profit is not unnecessarily disbursed in this way.

The ideal of single ownership from birth to slaughter is only achieved by a small fraction of farmers, e.g. the dairy farmer who has an intensive or semi-intensive beef unit which utilises farm bred bull calves or the large farm enterprise which includes both breeding and fattening units. Self-contained breeding and finishing units should also be developed where possible on both arable and grassland farms. When this is not possible producers should try to ensure that the animal passes through the ownership of only two, a breeder and finisher, between birth and slaughter, thus reducing additional charges to a minimum.

QUICK TURNOVER

A considerable amount of evidence available indicates that the lifetime profit made per animal slaughtered remains relatively constant regardless of age at slaughter. There is therefore little point in keeping animals to say 36 months of age when the same profit can be realised in 18 months. There is indeed a positive argument in favour of developing a system involving slaughter at 18 months since this should lead to a doubling of the profit realised over a 36-month period. This emphasises the need to produce animals of a type which can be brought to slaughter condition at a young age and at acceptable liveweights and this is discussed in Chapter 4. Various feeding systems are described later and all involve and require that the animals be fed to appetite on high-quality feeds. This is so because there is a direct relationship between food quality, food intake and animal performance. Maximum performance depends on achieving maximum feed intake and utilisation of nutrients. Poor-quality feed is digested slowly and the rate of passage through the gut is slow, therefore the animal feels full and lacks appetite. On the other hand, high-quality feed is rapidly digested, the animal feels empty or hungry and eats more, permitting an increase in the rate of liveweight gain. Feeding to appetite should therefore be practised with the possible exception of the latter stages of the all-concentrate feeding system. The use of high-quality feeds is therefore highly desirable, but they must not be used without regard to cost.

THE IMPORTANCE OF FOOD COSTS

It is generally agreed that food costs amount to some 60–70% of the total costs involved in beef production. Producers must, therefore, continually seek methods of reducing to a minimum the cost of feeds used and the food cost per lb of liveweight gain or carcase ultimately produced. Food cost per lb of carcase is affected by a number of factors but markedly by the rate of liveweight gain achieved between birth and slaughter and the degree of fatness at slaughter. These points are discussed later; the selection and use of low-cost feeds involves the calculation of "Food Unit Costs".

Food is used by the beef animal primarily as a source of energy and secondly as a source of protein. The energy value of foods is expressed in terms of Starch Equivalent (S.E.) and the protein value in terms of Digestible Crude Protein (D.C.P.). As the beef animal seldom requires more than 1·25 lb D.C.P. per day the major factor affecting food costs is the cost of the unit of Starch Equivalent used and this is determined by dividing the food cost per ton by its Starch Equivalent (see Table 3.1).

TABLE 3.1
CALCULATION OF STARCH EQUIVALENT UNIT COST

$$\text{S.E. unit cost} = \frac{\text{cost per ton}}{\text{S.E.}}$$

	S.E.	£/ton	S.E. unit cost
Barley	71·4	24·00	$\frac{24 \cdot 00}{71 \cdot 4} = £0 \cdot 34$

The foods used fall naturally into two groups, i.e. farm-grown bulky feeds such as grass and forage roots on the one hand and, on the other, concentrates which may be purchased or be farm grown, but have direct sale value. The cost of the unit of energy in farm-produced crops is largely a reflection of yield per acre since the cost of growing an acre of crop is fairly constant irrespective of yield although the cost of harvesting does increase with yield. The point is forcibly demonstrated with reference to the swede crop in Table 3.2.

TABLE 3.2
RELATIONSHIP OF YIELD PER ACRE OF SWEDES WITH COST PER TON OF ROOTS AND OF S.E. UNIT

Tons/acre	Cost/acre £	Cost/ton roots £	S.E. unit cost p
15	47	3·13	43
20	50	2·50	34
25	53	2·12	30
30	56	1·87	26
35	59	1·69	23

In the case of grass silage the S.E. unit cost is markedly affected also by the quality of the feed conserved as shown in Table 3.3.

TABLE 3.3
EFFECT OF QUALITY ON S.E. UNIT COST IN GRASS SILAGE
(8-ton crop)

S.E. of silage	S.E. unit cost p
8	28
10	23
12	19

These figures indicate that farmers should carefully examine their forage crop production technique and ability. In the longer term the farmer must find out which crops will produce the cheapest units of energy. In the short term, and when a farm-grown forage crop produces a poor yield, it is imperative that the cheapest possible alternative feeds be used to maintain food costs at a reasonable level. The purchase of feeds may then be involved and the unit cost calculation must again be done for the feeds on offer. In this case the *cost per ton delivered home* is divided by the appropriate Starch Equivalent value as shown in Table 3.4.

TABLE 3.4
S.E. UNIT COSTS—PURCHASED FEED

	S.E.	£/ton	S.E. unit cost p
Barley	71·4	24·00	34
Oats	59·5	20·75	35
Wheat	72·0	25·25	35
Maize	77·6	28·75	37
Flaked maize	84·0	32·12	38
Hay	30·0	15·00	50

This calculation indicates that barley offers the cheapest unit of energy in the given price situation. Foods which provide more expensive units must only be used when required for some specific purpose. For example, flaked maize is included because of its palatability in calf concentrate mixtures, but only the minimum quantity required for this purpose is used. Table 3.4 also indicates that hay is usually a "poor buy" when the energy unit cost is considered, so again only the minimum required should be purchased.

The purchase of additional protein for beef cattle is normally only necessary for inclusion in calf concentrates and when suckler cows are being wintered on very low-quality roughages. In such cases the cost of the unit of Digestible Crude Protein (D.C.P.) should be calculated by dividing the *cost per ton delivered home* by the D.C.P. of the feed as shown in Table 3.5.

TABLE 3.5
D.C.P. UNIT COSTS—PURCHASED FEEDS

	D.C.P.	£/ton	D.C.P. unit cost £
Dec. earthnut	42	54	1·29
Soya cake	40	55	1·38
White fishmeal	55	80	1·45

The inclusion of additional protein in rations for fattening cattle is usually unnecessary as it is seldom found that a ration calculated to provide sufficient energy to permit 2 lb daily liveweight gain does not also contain sufficient protein. No evidence has been produced to support the claim that the use of protein cake leads to an improvement in either the killing out percentage or carcase grade when the animal has been receiving sufficient energy. Furthermore, a simple energy unit cost calculation as shown in Table 3.6 emphasises that the use of a protein cake as a source of energy is ridiculously uneconomic.

TABLE 3.6
COMPARISON OF ENERGY UNIT COST IN BARLEY AND PROTEIN CAKE

	S.E.	£/ton	S.E. unit cost p
Barley	71·4	24·00	34
Dec. earthnut cake	73·0	54·00	74

ESTIMATION OF WINTER RATIONS

The first step on the farm is to estimate the total quantities of forage feed available for use during the winter. Having set aside maybe 10% to cover loss in store and the eventuality of a late spring the quantity to be fed per head daily is estimated. The amount of farm-grown or purchased concentrate required daily to ensure the desired rate of gain is then calculated. A simple example is as follows.

Friesian steers of 800 lb liveweight are required to gain 2 lb daily; 60 lb of grass silage is available per head per day, the S.E. being 10·0 and the D.C.P. 1·6, together with barley grain of S.E. 71·4 and D.C.P. 7·6.

	At 800 lb live wt		At 1000 lb live wt	
	S.E.	D.C.P.	S.E.	D.C.P.
Required daily*	9·50	1·15	11·00	1·25
Provided in 60 lb silage	6·00	0·96	6·00	0·96
Required from barley	3·50	0·19	5·00	0·29
Provided in—	5 lb barley		7 lb barley	
	3·57	0·38	5·00	0·53

* **Taken** from Table of Feeding Standards.

This exercise indicates that the cattle should make a daily liveweight gain of 2 lb if they receive 5 rising to 7 lb of barley in addition to the basic ration of 60 lb silage daily and they should achieve 1000 lb liveweight at the end of a 100-day feeding period. This performance will not always be achieved in practice for a variety of reasons. Occasionally the daily requirement of the animals may be underestimated but more frequently the nutritive value of roughages is overestimated. Ideally all batches of hay and silage should be analysed, but this is not always possible and values have frequently to be taken from tables giving the nutritive values of feeds. In the latter case the estimate should always err on the pessimistic side. For example, Nutritive Value Tables usually give starch equivalent values for various samples of hay ranging from 22 to 48, and 33 is usually quoted as the average value. Now farmers are loath to admit that they ever make any but the best of hay, but experience indicates that it is sound to use a value of 30 or even 25 unless there is clear evidence that a higher value is more appropriate. Optimistic over-valuation of roughages only leads to the need to use additional feed during the latter stages of the feeding period or disappointment in the rate of performance achieved by the animal.

It is also advisable to assume that the animals will not gain in liveweight immediately from the beginning of the feeding period. Animals which have been grazed on the farm and introduced gradually to winter rations while still grazing may begin to gain in weight when housed but animals which are bought in the market and immediately housed often make no progress for some two to three weeks. Furthermore, the rate of gain often declines as the animal reaches slaughter condition. It would therefore be sound to assume particularly with reference to cattle which have been bought in for fattening, for example at 800 lb liveweight, that they may only reach 967 lb liveweight after 100 days on feed arrived at thus: (14 days $\times 0) + (66 \times 2) + (20 \times 1{\cdot}75)$. There will, of course, be considerable variation between the performance of individual animals in a group fed in this way because the figures used can only refer to the "average animal". They cannot predict individual animal performance, nor do they cater for the fact that some individuals will eat more than others when group feeding is practised.

CHAPTER 4

THE IMPORTANCE OF THE TYPE OF ANIMAL AND OF RECORDING IN BEEF PRODUCTION

MOST textbooks concerned with cattle production have included a section on breeds which were conventionally classified into three groups: Beef, Dairy and Dual Purpose. This was sound when some breeds were clearly utilised solely for beef production, some for milk production and the remainder for both beef and milk. Such classification can, however, hardly be justified when although some breeds are clearly only utilised in beef production, others not only constitute the major part of the National Dairy Herd but also contribute some 75% of home-produced beef. The nomenclature of some breeds has indeed been openly changed, thus the Lincoln Red and Welsh Black formerly included under the Dual Purpose heading are now classified as beef breeds. Even the Friesian and Ayrshire breeds are now at least in effect Dual Purpose and it seems sensible to suggest that our breeds should simply be classified as either Beef or Dual Purpose.

Students who wish to delve into the history of our breeds or to study claims made on their behalf should consult standard works on the matter. It seems more important to consider here how we can produce the type of animal which is now required to enable the efficient, economical production of beef from the feeds which are available. Formerly emphasis was placed on the "early maturing" qualities of a breed, early maturity implying the ability to fatten at an early age in a situation where foods of moderate or poor quality were used. Our conventional beef breeds were very successfully developed against this background, producing animals which could be brought to slaughter condition at less than 2 years of age given diets which included pasture of moderate quality or hay and cereal straw in some quantity. The situation has now changed following an overall improvement in the quality of feeds available for beef cattle feeding and the requirement is now for animals which can continue to gain weight rapidly without developing excessive quantities of body fat at light weights. The ability of an animal to grow rapidly is important and fortunately this character is highly inherited. Thus a bull which gains weight rapidly will tend to sire calves which will also gain weight rapidly. The converse is also true. A slow-growing bull sires slow-growing calves and this is of great importance to the feeder who by chance purchases such animals. It is therefore necessary to identify individual bulls possessing the potential for rapid growth for use in both pure and cross-breeding, thus permitting the improvement of the type of animal made available to the feeder. The point is neatly illustrated by reference to the results of a Performance and Progeny Test.

Ten Beef Shorthorn bulls were taken into a centre at 3 weeks of age and were reared over a 400-day period on whole milk, concentrates, hay, swedes and grass silage. The performance of three bulls selected for progeny testing is summarised thus:

TABLE 4.1
PERFORMANCE OF THREE BULLS

Bull no.	Liveweight end of test lb	Liveweight gain during test lb	Daily gain over 400 days lb
2	1111	969	2·42
7	1008	869	2·17
10	966	875	2·19

Bull no. 2 made the highest liveweight gain on test and was rated "intermediate" for conformation. Bull no. 7 was rated best for conformation and made the lowest liveweight gain on test while no. 10 was rated poor for conformation and made a similar low liveweight gain to no. 7.

The three bulls were mated by artificial insemination to Ayrshire cows and the resulting calves were reared on the semi-intensive system described later, being slaughtered at 17 months of age. The results of this progeny test are summarised in Table 4.2.

TABLE 4.2
SUMMARY OF PROGENY TEST RESULTS

Sire no.	Liveweight lb	Age days	Carc. wt. lb	Dressing %	Gun as % side wt.	Price/head (1962)
2	928	537	546	58·8	52·4	£74·40
7	886	534	520	58·8	51·5	£71·20
10	876	527	515	59·0	52·6	£71·00

Gun = Round + rump + sirloin + best rib + hind shin.

The progeny of bull no. 2, which achieved the highest liveweight at about 400 days of age, were heavier at slaughter, yielded heavier carcases and realised over £3 more than the progeny of slower-growing bulls. There was no difference in carcase quality as measured by the percentage of the weight of side in the expensive cuts.

It is interesting to calculate the potential difference in value of progeny of these two bulls taking this at only £3 per head. Given natural mating, each bull may sire 40 calves per year. The difference in value of the progeny of the two bulls would then be £120 per year and taking the bull's life in the herd at 4 years this would multiply up to £480. It is further necessary to consider the potential difference in value of the two progeny groups assuming that the two sires were used at an Artificial Insemination Centre. This would be £36,000 if each bull sired 2000 calves per year over a 6-year period. Such figures give a modest estimate of the sums of money which might with profit be spent by the industry on the task of identifying rapid-growing sires. Work on this has developed considerably in the United Kingdom since 1960 and is now one of the functions of the Beef Improvement Services Section of the Meat and Livestock Commission (M.L.C.) which carries on the functions formerly performed by the Beef Recording Association (B.R.A.). This work involves the development of breed recording schemes and of central bull testing facilities.

BREED RECORDING SCHEMES

Such schemes are now supported by all the beef and several of our dual purpose breed societies. The object of such schemes is to supply reliable information on the performance of individual bulls and families within a breed and herd. Liveweight is recorded at birth when possible, at weaning and subsequently, thus permitting the calculation of liveweight at 200, 300 and 400 days of age. The data can be adjusted for sex of calf, age of dam, season of birth and preweaning management. Weighings are supervised by M.L.C. field officers and the results are returned to the breeder within a few days together with herd and breed averages for different age and sex groups. The breeder is thus provided with a measure of the performance of his stock and of his management. The 200-day weight gives an indication of the dam's milking ability while the 400-day weight gives a better measure of the sire's contribution to the growth potential of the calf and of the calf's own growth potential. The figures obtained must only be used to compare the performance of animals or families within a herd as any differences between herds may be due to differing standards of management. Large differences between herds may of course be used as a basis for questioning and examining management practice. The results obtained in all breed schemes will indeed show wide variations in performance both between

TABLE 4.3
LINCOLN RED CATTLE BREED AVERAGES* (LB) (1961–7)

Sex	Average	Range	Top ⅓	Bottom ⅓	Difference
		250-day weights			
Bulls	715	410–1050	785	570	215
Steers	585	365– 835	665	490	175
Heifers	555	305– 765	645	450	195
		300-day weights			
Bulls	825	690–1110	905	725	180
Steers	655	410– 895	760	555	205
Heifers	595	340– 850	685	500	185
		400-day weights			
Bulls	1085	825–1410	1210	980	230
Steers	835	465–1130	930	715	215
Heifers	735	400–1000	835	635	200
		500-day weights			
Bulls	1270	1035–1435	1370	1140	230
Steers	1010	750–1330	1120	905	215
Heifers	870	540–1135	975	765	210

* Rounded-off to nearest 5 lb: not corrected for age of dam.

and within herds and make possible the selection for pure breeding of individuals with good genetic potential for growth. It is generally suggested that replacement stock for the breeding herd should be selected from the top third on performance.

The range in performance found within a breed can be illustrated by reference to any one of the breed societies recording schemes. Some averages for the Lincoln Red for the period 1961–7 are given in Table 4.3.

When differences of the order shown in Table 4.3 occur, selection of replacement breeding stock from the top third on performance must lead to an improvement in the genetic potential of the animals for growth. Experience indicates so far that this can be achieved without sacrificing any other desirable qualities. Difficulty arises when it is necessary to make comparisons between individuals reared in different herds. Such comparison can only properly be made when the two individual animals enjoy the same environment. In practice this means that the animals to be compared must be reared for a period at a Performance Test Centre.

BULL PERFORMANCE TEST CENTRES

The testing of bulls at a centre permits the comparison of performance of animals from different herds in the test group. The breeder can also use the results obtained from his bull as a measure of his own management within his herd.

Conditions of entry and management are very similar at the five centres now operating in the United Kingdom. Bulls are taken in at about 7 months of age, being accepted only from recorded herds. Rigorous health standards are enforced. Bulls must exceed a given minimum liveweight at entry and must be of a type likely to meet licensing requirements. Bulls stay on test for about 6 months, performance being measured by the liveweight achieved at 400 days of age. This is a better basis for comparison than the daily liveweight gain during the test period as this may be grossly affected by the bulls, performance during the pre-test period. The period spent at the test centre may therefore be regarded as a compensation period which nullifies differences in pre-test management. The bulls are individually penned and are fed at a moderately generous level. Sugar beet pulp is presoaked and fed three times daily with concentrates, and hay is freely available. The bulls are scored for conformation at or near the end of the test period and the results with all the liveweight gain data obtained are published. Some results from an individual test given in Table 4.4 indicate the range and performance which are normally revealed.

TABLE 4.4
SUMMARY OF RESULTS FROM A STATION PERFORMANCE TEST

	Average	Range
Age at start, days	213	166–247
200-day wt., lb	439	340–580
Daily gain, birth to arrival, lb	1·9	1·4–2·4
Daily gain at centre, lb	3·1	2·7–3·4
Daily gain overall, lb	2·4	2·1–3·0
400-day wt., lb	1038	913–1271
Food consumption, lb/day:		
Concentrates	10·6	10·1–11·5
Sugar beet pulp	1·9	1·8–2·1
Hay	5·8	5·5–6·3

Attention is drawn particularly to the range of 358 lb in the 400-day weight which confirms that there is ample scope for selection of individuals with good genetic potential for growth. The use of this information, together with the results obtained from herd recording, enables the breeder to improve the genetic potential for growth of his stock. Commercial breeders and the Artificial Insemination Centres may also benefit immediately in that they can buy performance tested bulls of proven merit which are not returned to pure breeding.

RECORDING IN COMMERCIAL BREEDING HERDS

The place of recording in pure breeding herds has now been established and animals of proven genetic potential for growth should now become available to the benefit of the commercial breeder. Recording makes this possible and can similarly be used in turn by the commercial breeder as an aid in the selection of breeding replacements within his herd and, equally important, help in increasing efficiency of management and the profitability of the enterprise. In addition to financial data records should be kept of the liveweight of calves at birth, at turnout or in spring in outwintered herds, at weaning and at time of sale. Details must also be recorded concerning weights of foods consumed in winter and of the acreage required for grazing.

The liveweight data enable calculation of the calf's 200-day weight. This provides a good measure of the milking ability of the dam and taken with the liveweight at weaning and at sale gives a factual basis for the culling of cows. In this context it is interesting to note that survey results indicate a more rapid turnover of cows in the more profitable herds, such culling being done on the basis of calf liveweight at weaning. Heavier culling leads to an increase in the herd depreciation figure per cow per year but also to an increase in profitability because it has a sound factual basis. Cows can be so culled on the basis of their first one or two calf weaning weights because fortunately weaning weight is highly repeatable, which justifies the culling of cows on the basis of the weaning weight of the first one or at the most two calves. Comparisons can also be made between the progeny of different sires and of different types of cow and the effect of calving at different seasons can be measured. The relationship between these factors and profitability was clearly indicated in the results of a B.R.A. study of data from recorded suckler herds over the period 1966 to 1968. In this study comparisons were made between the top and bottom thirds of producers ranked according to the profitability of the enterprise. It was demonstrated that: "Results from study groups show the close relationship that exists between daily liveweight gain of the calf and gross margin per cow; for every 0·1 lb increase in calf daily liveweight gain the gross margin per cow increased by £1·18." Also: "The difference in the average weaning weight of calves between the top and bottom third herds was 108 lb, the difference in net output was £6 per cow." And: "Calves in the top third herds gained 0·3 lb more per day than calves in the bottom third."

These findings emphasise the close relationship which exists between profitability and the genetic potential for liveweight gain possessed by the calves. In turn this implies the need to use a bull of proven merit for liveweight gain and it is suggested that the sire used should have achieved a liveweight of at least 1100 lb at 400 days of age. It must be emphasised that it is the genetic potential of the individual bull and not his breed which is important, but bulls possessing this quality are available from most of our breeds as is illustrated by the 400-day liveweight data produced by M.L.C. in September 1969 and given in Table 4.5.

TABLE 4.5
400-DAY WEIGHTS (LB) FOR BULLS AS RECORDED TO SEPTEMBER 1969

Breed	No.	Ave.	Range
Charolais	68	1134	871–1455
South Devon	150	1126	780–1445
Devon	196	1096	610–1375
Lincoln Red	691	1062	825–1550
Sussex	87	1036	600–1305
Hereford	2703	994	650–1350
Welsh Black	17	984	610–1174
Aberdeen Angus	1484	927	630–1350
Beef Shorthorn	124	903	640–1165
Galloway	46	766	475– 925
Belted Galloway	19	701	555– 980

Commercial breeders must note carefully that the publication of such a table of figures does NOT imply that they should simply concentrate on using bulls from say the Charolais, South Devon and Devon breeds only. They must note the big range in 400-day liveweight within each breed and select a bull which possesses not only the necessary potential for gain but also any other desirable qualities which may be considered an attribute of any given breed.

Now it has for long been said that "the bull is half the herd", but it is equally true that the individual calf received 50% of its potential for growth from its dam. The dam's genetic potential for growth is therefore also very important, but she must possess other qualities and recording indicates the type of cow which is most successful in a given environment. In addition to potential for liveweight gain the suckler cow must possess the ability to milk well, longevity, the ability for easy calving and hardiness appropriate to her environment. It is questionable whether many suckler cows now possess all these qualities. In too many cases the commercial breeder has repeatedly retained home-bred heifer calves sired by a beef bull of unproven merit for use as breeding cows. The cow thus bred may well be hardy and of good conformation, but in the absence of records it has not been possible to select for milk yield and potential for liveweight gain. As a result the calves presented at sales may be small and of an early-maturing type which fatten at light weights. It therefore seems reasonable to suggest that effort be made to return to the use of a first beef cross dairy type of cow for use in suckler herds. The Blue Grey cow was a conventional example of such a type sired by a White Cumberland Dual Purpose Shorthorn bull and out of a Galloway cow. This Blue Grey is rapidly disappearing from the farming scene as the Friesian completes the rout of the old Dual Purpose Shorthorn from Cumberland which was started by the Ayrshire in the 1930s. Many suggest that the Hereford cross Friesian cow offers a solution. This cross combines the beefing qualities, growth potential and hardiness of the Hereford with the milking qualities, growth potential and, some would add, beefing qualities of the Friesian. Adequately fed, the Hereford Friesian cow produces a vigorous calf of good birth rate, provides milk to match the growth potential of the calf which achieves good liveweight at weaning and goes forward to the feeder with the ability to grow on rapidly to a good liveweight before being slaughtered. The Hereford cross Friesian also possesses the considerable attribute of availability since the Friesian comprises some 80% of the National Dairy Herd.

The argument in favour of using a beef cross dairy cow was supported by the results of the B.R.A. Suckler Cow Study already quoted and continued by the M.L.C. One pertinent finding emerging from this continued study was to the effect that steer calves out of beef cross Friesian cows in low ground herds were on average 32 lb heavier at 200 days of age than calves out of beef type cows. In upland and hill herds the difference in 200-day rate was 19 lb and 7 lb respectively. The figures clearly suggest the use of a beef cross Friesian cow not only in low ground herds but also in upland and hill herds where the liveweight advantage although small is still real. Furthermore, the calf out of the dairy cross cow will possess better growth potential and will be more readily sold than the early-maturing type of calf.

The reduced advantage in calf liveweight at 200 days found on hill and upland farms may of course be due to inadequate feeding resulting in a reduction in both calf birth weight and milk yield. This implies the need to examine feeding levels in hill and uplands herds, particularly when beef cross dairy type cows are used. It may further be suggested that this type of cow is not sufficiently "hardy" for success in the upland environment and it seems appropriate to consider briefly at least some aspects of the contentious topic, hardiness.

It is commonly claimed that a small framed animal is particularly suited to marginal conditions. Is this true, and if so why? It seems reasonable to suggest that the claim can be substantiated in areas where the herbage and conserved roughage are deficient in an individual mineral or minerals. Such conditions may well prohibit the use of a large framed cow while a small framed animal may be relatively successful. But the latter type of cow would produce a small framed calf which would have a poor potential for growth. It is clear that if such circumstances do prevail, then the constructive steps to take are first to ascertain the mineral and vitamin status of the herbage and to correct any deficiencies found by using an appropriate supplement. A larger framed cow may then be successfully introduced provided that she can be adequately fed to support the higher yield of milk required by her more rapidly growing calf. In other words, if hardiness is equated with the ability to withstand some degree of malnutrition then the need for such hardiness no longer exists if malnutrition is corrected. It is important to stress that such malnutrition may not solely refer to the mineral and vitamin content of the diet but also to energy and occasionally to protein.

Hardiness is also often equated with coat type, thus it is claimed that the Galloway and the Highland cow are hardy because they grow a long outer hairy coat which sheds rain, over a mossy under coat which helps to retain body heat. These two breeds therefore appear to be suited to withstand wet cold conditions. Others argue, however, that animals from most breeds will grow a coat appropriate to the weather of the area in which they are reared and that nutrition, not coat type, is of prime significance. The subject is contentious and is of greater significance when cows are outwintered. It is, however, clear, as already indicated, that an objective should be to find for each environment a cow capable of producing a vigorous calf and ample milk to support fully the calf's potential for growth. Suitable examples should be obtained for use in most areas from beef dairy crosses such as the Hereford Friesian, Hereford Ayrshire, Galloway Friesian and South Devon Galloway. These should all produce a type of calf suited to meet the requirements of the low ground feeder.

RECORDING IN THE FATTENING PERIOD

The recording of food consumption and of liveweight as an aid to efficient management during the fattening period has not yet been widely adopted, maybe because the experienced cattleman claims that he can competently assess by eye the progress made by the animal. This claim is, however, often put in doubt when a weighing machine is regularly used.

Routine weighing shows that when cattle are bought in for fattening a number are often included which do not increase in liveweight, this occurring however skilful the buyer. Such animals often appear thrifty and are not spotted by the stockman. They consume food throughout the fattening period which may extend to 20 weeks and costs £20 or more, but they show little or no return in terms of liveweight gains. This food cost must be borne by the rest of the group. The presence of such an animal is only revealed by routine weighing and it can then be sold for slaughter before excessive feed costs are incurred.

Routine weighing should also be used to reduce food costs as the animals reach slaughter condition when the rate of liveweight gain falls while food consumption continues at the full level. Efficiency of food conversion must then fall and food costs per pound of liveweight gain rise. Animals should be slaughtered as soon as there is a noticeable fall in the rate of gain and the animal is in a marketable condition. This can only be done satisfactorily when a weighing machine is used since the change in rate of liveweight gain cannot be detected with certainty by eye even by the experienced stockman. The labour costs associated with weighing must be kept to a minimum and this can only be achieved when pen design and layout permit efficient stock movement and weighing. The cost of the weighing machine is of little significance since an efficient and robust machine incorporating an excellent handling crate can be purchased for the price of two fat cattle.

The need for such recording is emphasised by the results obtained from most surveys of cattle fattening enterprises. Some results from one survey are given in Table 4.6.

TABLE 4.6
SEMI-INTENSIVE GRASS/CEREAL BEEF PERFORMANCE 1968/9

	No. of cattle	No. of farms	Weight (lb) at		No. of days	DLWG (lb)	Food cost per lb LWG p
			Yarding	Slaughter			
Average	1708	58	714	1036	166	1·9	8
Range			600–836	880–1180	124–260	1·0–2·8	4–16½
Top ⅓			769	1044	133	2·1	7
Bottom ⅓			658	1012	207	1·5	10

It is almost certain that the bottom third of producers in this survey did not make a direct profit on cattle fattening as their food costs per pound liveweight gain just equalled the return of 10p per pound liveweight. This would not be apparent in the absence of the necessary records, nor would it be possible to identify the reasons for the poor results. Detailed records are essential before poor results can be attributed to factors such as: type of animal, high cost of farm-produced feeds, use of expensive purchased feeds, or animals kept too long or until over-fat.

THE STUDY GROUP APPROACH

The use of records is now developing in all phases of beef production. At the breeding level this enables the production of the type of animal required with the ability to gain weight rapidly. At the commercial breeding and fattening stages it permits measurement of management ability in terms of the production and procurement of low-cost feed units essential to a low food cost per pound of liveweight gain. Over all, recording assists in the improvement of the efficiency and profitability of beef production. The Study Group approach is a recent development which aims to assist this improvement in efficiency. A Study Group is formed from a number of farmers who are concerned in one specific phase of beef production and forms a focal point for the discussion of results, advice and the exchange of information. They also act as a hub for new developments. The movement is commendable from all viewpoints and should spread rapidly.

CHAPTER 5

CALF REARING

AT FIRST glance it may appear that a wide variety of calf-rearing systems are practised, but they readily fall into two main groups thus: Natural and Artificial rearing or feeding systems. The "Natural" or "Single Suckling System" is patently the oldest method of all, the cow suckling its calf until either the flow of milk dries up or the calf satisfies its requirements from grazing and stops sucking. Efforts have been made from time to time to increase the output of calves per cow by fostering on the cow an additional calf or calves, resulting in the Double and Multiple suckling methods of rearing respectively.

Natural rearing systems are clearly not generally acceptable in dairy herds where the emphasis is on the sale of the maximum possible volume of milk per cow. Artificial rearing systems are required and have been developed. These usually involve the use of a restricted volume of cows' milk and the feeding of a milk substitute from a bucket unless and until a satisfactory and economical suckling machine becomes available. In addition the calf is usually taken from its dam at or very soon after birth. Thus the conventional approach to calf rearing until the late 1940s, when beef production began to achieve its present significance, implied that Natural systems were to be used for rearing beef calves while Artificial systems were accepted as being necessary and indeed satisfactory for rearing dairy heifer replacement calves. Such an arbitrary distinction is clearly no longer acceptable or applicable when over one million bull calves born in dairy herds are reared to be slaughtered for beef production. These calves must be reared artificially, but it must be questioned whether any given system which is acceptable for rearing dairy heifers is the best for rearing an animal destined for the butcher's block. The background to the rearing of dairy heifers so often tends to be tinged with parsimony. Thus one system may be judged against another according to the "food costs to 12 weeks of age" and not the "food costs per pound liveweight at 12 weeks of age" and the probable significance of rate of liveweight gain during early life in the beef calf tends to be overlooked. Many dairymen contend that the heifer should be fed moderately rather than generously, thus encouraging the ultimate conversion of food into milk rather than flesh. This contention received some support from experimental work at a number of centres, but more recent work suggests that there can be a place for the more generous treatment of dairy heifers. Now whatever the optimum plane of nutrition for the dairy heifer may be, there is no doubt as to the optimum for the beef calf. Tradition teaches that the calf being reared for beef should be reared so that it never suffers a check to growth and abounds in sayings such as: "The beef animal should never lose its calf flesh" and "The dearest food to give to a beef animal is beefsteak". The beef cattleman is adamant that the animal being reared for slaughter should receive the best possible treatment and the results of experimentation support his claim. Experience indicates that single suckled calves usually gain at the rate of 1·5 lb daily or more to 12 weeks of age whereas artificially reared calves do well to achieve a daily gain of 1·2 lb over this period. It is therefore necessary to ensure that artificial rearing systems be practised as efficiently as possible and indeed they must be improved before calves so reared do as well as suckled calves and fully realise their potential for growth. These rearing systems must then be examined in detail, but before so doing it is appropriate to deal with a number of factors which affect the success of all rearing systems.

FACTORS AFFECTING SUCCESSFUL CALF REARING

The Influence of Pre-natal Nutrition

Ideally calves should be full of vigour at birth and, provided they are, should be above average liveweight for their breed. But note that vigour is more important than mere weight. It is easier to rear a small calf which is full of vigour than a calf of great liveweight which is soft and sloppy when born. Liveweight and vigour at birth largely reflect the plane of nutrition enjoyed in the uterus during the last 8 weeks or so before birth. The uterine plane of nutrition should be satisfactory in the dairy cow provided that she has been steamed up properly and her diet has included an adequate supply of minerals and vitamins in addition to energy and protein. This is often not so in commercial beef breeding herds when undue importance may be placed on the reduction of winter feed costs to the minimum. This may result in the cow receiving a diet which is sub-optimal in energy, protein, vitamins and minerals. In turn this results in the birth of puny calves lacking any semblance of vigour, which have to be held up to the teat to suck and are prone to succumb to any disease which prevails. One classical case occurred in areas where the traditional diet for the cow consisted of swedes and oat straw both of which are markedly deficient in vitamin E, leading to the occurrence of muscular dystrophy in the calves. The occurrence of muscular dystrophy has been much reduced following the addition of 20 lb grass silage or wet grains to the basic swede and straw ration for 6 weeks before calving. The use of these feeds steps up the energy, protein and usually the vitamin E levels in the cow's diet. This usually effects an increase in birthweight and the vigour of calves born. If muscular dystrophy still occurs, recourse has in addition to be made to the administration under veterinary direction of either vitamin E or selenium. The object lesson of this is: examine the diet of the cow if small weakly calves are born.

The Importance of Feeding Colostrum

Colostrum is the highly coloured "milk" produced immediately after calving. It is variously named "New Milk", "Beastings" or "Fore Milk" in different areas. It differs from normal milk in chemical composition as follows:

	Colostrum (1st milking)	Normal milk
Water	73·00	87·50
Milk fat	3·50	3·75
Casein	2·75	3·00
Albumin and globulin	16·50	0·50
Sugar	3·00	4·50
Mineral	1·25	0·75

Colostrum is obviously much richer in protein and particularly in albumin and globulin, which on clotting form a soft curd, whereas casein forms a hard knotty curd. The latter can lead to mechanical irritation of the gut wall, indigestion and scouring. Colostrum is also richer in minerals, especially calcium and phosphorus, and in vitamin A. It has a gentle purgative action which induces the normal functioning of the gut wall. Chemical analysis does not, however, reveal the most important value of colostrum, which rests in its antibody content. The antibodies are largely associated with the globulin fraction and their function is to help prevent *Escherichia coli* and other intestinal bacteria from invading the body. The antibodies can only pass through the gut wall during the first 24–36 hours of life. Colostrum should therefore be fed to the calf as soon as possible after birth and for 2 days thereafter. In the odd case when the dam's colostrum is not available, it may be taken from a newly calved cow or from a supply which is held in the farm cold store and is regularly replaced. If no colostrum is available the following mixture, which has approximately the same chemical composition as colostrum, can be made up and fed:

1½ pints milk
½ pint warm water
1 raw egg
2 teaspoons castor oil.

This mixture has no antibody content and veterinary advice should be obtained regarding the use of antibiotics until the calf is about 10 days of age, when it begins to produce its own antibodies.

The Calf's Digestive System and the Composition of Milk Substitutes

The ideal milk substitute should approximate to cow's milk in composition, but the production of such a substitute is fraught with difficulties and indeed it may be claimed that the ideal substitute is yet to be produced. Like cow's milk, a satisfactory substitute must inevitably be related to the nature of the calf's digestive system. The calf does not secrete enzymes capable of digesting carbohydrates other than lactose (milk sugar). Other carbohydrates are, of course, digested by bacteria in the rumen when it begins to function at about 3 weeks of age. However, the closure of the oesophageal groove is stimulated by milk up to about 12 weeks of age. Liquid diets bypass the rumen and must therefore contain lactose, glucose and fat as sources of energy. Other carbohydrates including starch are wasted and may indeed be harmful, inducing scouring if they pass along the gut to suffer bacterial fermentation in the colon. Glucose cannot be used in quantity as the feeding of more than 250 g daily leads to scouring and unthriftiness in calves. Hence, fat is essential to maintain the energy intake of calves at a satisfactory level. Mother Nature, of course, may be given the credit for including fat in milk for this purpose. Man proceeds to separate this fat from milk for his own use in butter and cheese or as cream. The remaining "separated" or "skim milk", butter milk and whey, all of which are used as bases for calf milk substitute manufacture, are clearly then deficient in fat as compared with whole milk. This is illustrated by the following analytical results:

	D.M.	C.P.	E.E.	N.F.E.	Ash.	S.E.
Whole milk	12·8	3·4	3·9	4·8	0·7	17·1
Separated milk	9·4	3·5	0·1	5·0	0·8	8·3
Butter milk	9·2	3·6	0·8	4·1	0·7	9·2
Whey	6·6	0·7	0·2	5·0	0·7	6·1

The problem of raising the energy content of these milk by-products has been difficult. The fats or oils used must be cheaper than butter fat, they must be relatively saturated since the inclusion of unsaturated fats interferes with the utilisation of vitamin E, leading to the occurrence of muscular dystrophy, it must be possible to ensure that they do not go rancid when the "milk" powder is stored and finally when the milk substitute is reconstituted the fat globule size must be less than 0·004 mm in diameter otherwise absorption in the gut is reduced. During recent years success has been achieved in including beef tallow and lard in milk substitutes which are now available containing from 17 to 22% fat. When these are reconstituted at the conventional rate of 1 lb per gallon of water the resulting substitute thus contains 1·7 to 2·2% fat according to the product used. The fat content can be raised by increasing the concentration in the reconstituted liquid and this practice will be found later to be an integral part of "once per day feeding".

Another difficulty connected with the production of milk substitutes concerns the calf's dependence on an adequate supply of milk protein to enable it to resist infection by *E. coli*. Milk by-products must be dried to permit economic transportation, but the milk protein is denatured if separated milk is over-heated during the drying process. It is now accepted that spray drying following only mild pre-heating has least effect on milk protein. This is, therefore, the method of choice in the production of milk substitutes.

The Physical Nature and Chemical Composition of Calf Concentrates

Palatability is the first essential quality of concentrates fed to calves. This is especially important in the case of artificially reared beef calves which must be encouraged to consume concentrates in quantity at an early age when they convert feed most efficiently and because they must be enabled to grow to their full potential. Finely ground and dusty feeds induce coughing and respiratory troubles and are unpalatable. Coarse flaky ingredients are preferred and indeed a phrase such as "snap, crackle and pop" could well be used as a sales slogan with reference to calf feed as well as human breakfast cereals. Finely ground feeds suffer the additional disadvantage of very rapid digestion in the calf's gut, which may result in excessive gas production, leading to indigestion and bloat. Flaky ingredients do not appear to suffer from this disadvantage. The concentrate mixture should have a high energy content and a Crude Protein of 16% gives satisfactory results up to 12 weeks of age, when the Crude Protein content can be reduced to 13% for the subsequent rearing period. Mixtures which give satisfactory results are given on pages 43 and 59.

REARING METHODS

It is more appropriate to discuss suckling methods of rearing in detail together with the management of the suckler herd. This is done in Chapter 6, but it is convenient at this stage to discuss some advantages and disadvantages of suckling systems.

Single Suckling

No other method of calf rearing gives better or indeed as good results as single suckling when the growth of the calf is of prime consideration. This method enjoys outstanding advantages thus: the calf receives colostrum at the right time and it subsequently receives milk of the correct composition. The milk is at the optimum temperature, body heat, and thus does not require the expenditure of any heat to raise the feed to body temperature in the gut. The food is free from any bacterial infection provided that the udder is healthy, and little or no labour is required to teach the calf how to feed in that it suckles naturally. Finally, the calf can take its feed in small quantities at frequent intervals and the feed passes naturally into the abomasum, sucking of milk efficiently stimulating the closure of the oesophageal groove.

Single suckling does, however, suffer the serious disadvantage of high costs in that the dam must be maintained for the whole year and at the very best only one weaned calf is produced per cow per year. The system has traditionally been practised in areas where there are no facilities for the sale of liquid milk and particularly in hill and upland areas where land rentals are low. However, even under these conditions it has been and is still necessary to subsidise this method of calf production. In 1970 the "Hill Cow" attracted a subsidy of £18·75 per year and in addition subsidies of £11·25 and £9·00 were paid per steer and heifer calf produced. The system can hardly be regarded as financially sound so long as existing costs and cattle prices prevail.

Double Suckling

Double suckling is sometimes recommended as the obvious way of reducing the costs of suckled calf production. An additional calf is bought and fostered on to the cow, thus spreading the costs of cow maintenance over two calves. Unfortunately this system seldom succeeds in practice. The procurement of additional calves of the right type and at the correct time is very difficult to achieve, particularly in hill and upland areas where arrangements cannot be made with neighbouring dairy farmers. Resort may be made to purchase in the nearest market, but this practice often results in the "buying-in of disease" and outbreaks of scour. When calves can be obtained, fostering makes considerable demands on labour and a good patient stockman is a prerequisite for success. Furthermore, it is essential to feed the cow at the appropriate level to ensure a supply of milk adequate for two calves. For some reason many stockmen are loath to do this under these conditions. Conventional diets such as 60 lb swedes, 10 lb straw and 4 lb oats (OR 60 lb silage and 4 lb. barley) provide for maintenance and the production of 1 gallon of milk daily by the housed cow. It is therefore necessary to raise the grain level by 4 lb daily to provide for the production of another gallon of milk for the second calf and such rations may be adequate for spring calving cows. However, calves born earlier in the winter will each require 2 gallons milk daily before they are turned out in spring. The cow will therefore require a ration such as 60 lb swedes, 10 lb straw plus *14 lb grain or concentrate* to provide for the production of 4 gallons of milk daily. Double suckled cows are seldom fed at these levels, possibly because the farmer is not sure that the additional feed costs will be recovered. Both calves are under-fed during the winter period and the final result is the presentation of two poor animals in lieu of one good calf at sale time. The system can be successful when additional calves can be obtained and the cow is capable of yielding 4 gallons of milk daily and is fed adequately, but these conditions seldom prevail.

Multiple Suckling

Multiple suckling is successfully practised by some calf rearers and they are usually found on lowground farms where a supply of calves can be obtained from neighbouring dairy farmers. A good milking cow is essential and is required to suckle up to eight calves to 12 or 14 weeks of age per lactation. The cow may suckle a group of three calves for 14 weeks followed by a second group of three and then a group of two for subsequent 14-week periods. There is clearly no place in this system for the obstreperous cow which does not submit readily to fostered calves. Any such cow should be sold. Skilled, patient labour is, however, still essential to ensure that all calves obtain an adequate supply of milk. Cows and calves are penned separately, the cows being taken in to the calf pens twice or three times daily for suckling. Concentrates and hay are made available to the calves from 2 weeks of age. A group of calves are weaned at 12–14 weeks of age provided that the next group of calves have become available. Weaning should not be abrupt. The new group of calves are allowed to suckle until the stockman considers that they have consumed sufficient milk. The group of older calves then strip out the cow. Over a week the younger group are allowed to suckle for a longer period and the group of older calves are thus gradually weaned.

This system is used by some dairy farmers who wish to raise their steer calves for beef production and wish to retain a good breeding cow which may have lost a quarter through physical damage, e.g. by being torn on barbed wire.

A Conventional Twice Daily Feeding System

The following system has been used successfully for a number of years in North Scotland. Similar systems have been developed elsewhere which vary in detail and usually with reference to the volume of whole milk and milk substitute used and in the level of concentrate intake achieved before the calf is weaned.

After receiving colostrum for 3–4 days whole milk is fed, rising to 6 pints daily at the end of the week. The volume of milk and substitute is then increased as follows:

Week	1	2	3	4	5	6	7	8
Milk/substitute pints daily	6	7	8	9	10	11	12	12

When milk is available on the rearing farm the volume fed per head can with advantage reach 20 gallons and should not be reduced below a minimum of 10 gallons. When 20 gallons is given per calf, a low fat milk substitute can subsequently be used. When whole milk is not available in the rearing unit, care should be taken to accept only strong vigorous calves and it is imperative that they receive a high fat milk substitute.

Water, good hay and concentrates should be made available during the second week, concentrates being fed to appetite. Calves are weaned when the average daily intake for the group reaches 2·5 lb. Weaning at a given age is often advised, but such practice is not sound taking no account of the great variation in vigour among calves of a given age. Calves should be weaned when experience shows that they will not suffer a check when milk substitute is withdrawn. They very rarely do when weaned at a concentrate intake level of 2·5 lb daily. Individually penned calves may be successfully weaned when they consume less than 2·5 lb concentrate daily, but careful observation shows that odd calves in a group of four or six often suffer a bad check if the group is weaned when average concentrate intake is less than 2·5 lb daily. After weaning, concentrate intake is allowed to increase with appetite until daily intake reaches 6 lb and is then held at that level. A suitable concentrate mixture to use to this stage is:

5 cwt Decorticated expeller earthnut flakes
5 cwt Flaked maize
6 cwt Bruised oats
3 cwt Flaked or bruised barley
1 cwt Broad Bran
Vitamin A to supply 500 I.U. per lb
Vitamin B to supply 75 I.U. per lb
Minerals including a magnesium-rich supplement

This system has proved very satisfactory for the rearing of calves which are to continue in the "Intensive" or "Semi-intensive" systems of beef production which are described later.

Once per Day Feeding System

This system of calf rearing has been developed only during recent years and has been widely adopted particularly for the rearing of dairy heifers. The following type of feeding plan is used:

	Day							
	1	2	3	4	5	6	7–30	30–35
Glucose (oz) in 2 or 3 feeds	8–12							
17% fat milk substitute	0	3½	4	7½	10	12½	15	Gradually wean
Ounces once per day in warm water (pints)	4–6	4	5	5	5	5	5	0

(15 oz in 5 pints ≡ 1·5 lb per gallon)

D

Drinking water must always be on offer and good hay and concentrates are made available from 4 days of age. The major advantage achieved is in labour saving in that feed mixing and bucket washing are only required once daily. The time of substitute feeding is immaterial, but should be at the same time daily. To some extent the timing can therefore be fitted in to match the availability of the stockman. The milk substitute is fed at a stronger concentration than that used in the conventional twice daily feeding system.

The system may be criticised in that it may encourage the practice of examining calves once daily only when they require more frequent attention. Although accepted as satisfactory for dairy heifers, the system has not yet been fully proven for the rearing of beef calves.

5½-day Feeding System

This system has been developed for use in areas where no skilled labour is available at weekends. It is claimed that calves suffer less when they do not receive milk substitute at the weekend than when they are then fed by unskilled and probably careless relief workers. Feeding on 5½ days is recommended for use from 10 days of age, the system being as follows:

Day	2	3	4	5–9	10–28		
					Mon.–Fri.	Sat.	Sun.
No. of feeds daily	2	2	2	2	2	1	–
17% substitute (oz)	1½	3	4½	6	8¾	8¾	–
Warm water (pints)	3	3	3	3	3½	3½	–

(8·75 oz in 3·5 pints ≡ 1·25 lb/gallon)

Water, hay and concentrates must be freely available from 4 days of age. The system is said to be satisfactory for dairy heifers but cannot yet be recommended for beef calves. The possibility of the calf suffering a bad check during the first weeks of life is clearly greater with this system. There would appear to be considerable risk of calves not being properly inspected at weekends in the absence of skilled stockmen.

Machine Feeding Systems

The successful use of all bucket feeding systems depends upon the availability of skilled stockmen, but unfortunately men of this type become more and more hard to find and feeding systems such as the "once per day" system have been developed in an attempt to mitigate the situation. Another possibility is to devise automatic feeding machines which would remove the need for the hand-mixing of substitute and the time-consuming task of washing buckets. Such machines have now been available for a number of years; they vary in price from about £150 to £800. They all automatically mix milk substitute powder and warm water to a specified concentration which may be adjustable. Most lower priced machines dispense the liquid feed through one teat which is claimed to satisfy at least fifteen calves. Additional teat assemblies can be provided on most machines at an extra cost. The highest priced machine offers one teat per calf fed in the group and involves pumping pre-mixed substitute through a ring main running round the calf pens. The teats are presented either automatically or manually to the calves, permitting cleaning of the ring main when the teats are withdrawn from the pen. The principal advantage claimed for all such machines is clearly that of labour saving and particularly that the stockman is relieved of the strict timing routine which is essential in bucket feeding systems. Most claim also an improvement in calf performance due to the constant availability of milk substitute.

Cost is obviously a big disadvantage. Others have been claimed after usage of various machines. The most important concerning the rearing of calves for beef concerns the efficacy of using one teat to feed a group consisting of fifteen calves. In theory each calf in the group should be able to obtain an adequate volume of milk substitute. In practice sometimes they do not. A glutton often spends considerable time drinking and unfortunately may go further and literally "police" or guard the teat, preventing other calves from sucking. This results in the development of a number of ill-thriven calves in the group which must be left on the machine after the remainder have been weaned. The batch must not be made up with additional bought-in calves. This would invite cross-infection and ill health would probably follow. Constant attention by the stockman would obviate this development, but the practice would also annul claims concerning labour economy. This latter claim may also be questioned on the grounds that the stockman must additionally acquire some expertise as a mechanical, electrical or electronic fitter. The time spent on maintenance and machine cleaning may well equal that spent on a conventional bucket system.

It is difficult to predict the future, but it may well be that the wide adoption of the machine system will await the development of a lower priced and easily maintained system. Ultimate success with beef calves will certainly seem to depend on the availability of one teat per calf in the group.

Management of the Bought-in Calf

All calves should be carefully examined and any showing signs of a discharge from nose or eyes, a wet navel, pneumonia, a harsh coat, scour or other signs of ill health should be rejected. The calf should have a clean bright coat, a clear eye and be full of vigour. Ideally calves should be bought directly from the farm on which they are born and advice should be taken from the veterinary surgeon as to which farms are thought to be free from disease, especially salmonella. The use of the open market should be avoided and the identity of a reputable dealer should be established in case his assistance is required.

On arrival home the calf should be housed in an individual pen or crate and be swabbed for salmonella, arrangements having been made for testing with the veterinary surgeon. The method of feeding on arrival should vary according to buying practice. When calves are actually bought on the farm of birth, information on previous feeding practice and level achieved should be obtained and the calf should be taken straight on at that level provided it is transported in a draught-free van. The feeding level should only be reduced if there are obvious reasons for doing this. Calves which have travelled a long distance may on arrival be suffering from hunger and dehydration. Standard practice is to offer milk diluted with 75% water at the first feed and to increase the concentration to whole milk over the next two or three feeds. If the calf is suffering badly from dehydration the first drink given may consist of an electrolytic salt solution or of 4 oz glucose in 2 pints of water. The need to adopt these various practices should be discussed with the veterinary surgeon.

The calves should be moved into pens holding four or six animals when negative results are obtained from the salmonella test or when they reach 3 weeks of age. Group feeding is desirable in that it introduces an element of competition at the trough and the vigorous feeder encourages the slow feeder to achieve the desired level of concentrate intake, which then rises more quickly than when individual penning is practised. The provision of a water bowl in each pen is also necessary to ensure liberal consumption of concentrates.

Calf Housing

The initial requirements are that the calf house should be warm, dry and free from draughts. In a controlled environment house the temperature should be held at about 65°F, the relative humidity at 80 and ventilation should provide 60 ft^3 of air per calf per minute. When these standards cannot be achieved it is more important to avoid wide fluctuations in temperature than to achieve a constant temperature of say 65°F. Thus it would be preferable to accept a constant temperature of 50°F rather than 60°F during the day time which might fall to say 40°F at night.

If straw is in short supply the provision of slatted duck boards helps to keep the bed area dry.

Calf Subsidy

The conditions are summarised in the M.L.C. Meat and Livestock Statistics as follows:

"Subsidy is payable either for steer and heifer calves of beef type (Stage A), or for steers and heifers of any breed which have been slaughtered for beef (Stage B).

Stage A

"To qualify for Stage A, calves must:

(a) have been born in the United Kingdom;

(b) have been properly reared;
(c) be suitable either for further rearing for beef production or, if heifer calves, for use for breeding for beef production;
(d) be likely to yield reasonable good quality beef if slaughtered either immediately or after further rearing and fattening.

"Application must be made early enough for animals to be inspected and certified before they have cut their first permanent incisor tooth. Heifer calves of the Jersey, Guernsey, Friesian and Ayrshire breeds, and of crosses between these breeds, are not eligible. The rates of subsidy for calves born after 1st January 1967 are £9·00 and £11·25 per head respectively for heifers and steers.

Stage B

"To qualify for stage B, the carcase must be presented at an approved deadweight centre at the same time as it is presented for certification for a fatstock guarantee payment, and it must be of a standard eligible for such a payment. The animal or carcase must not have been imported and must not have been previously certified for the calf subsidy. Subject to these conditions, carcases of fat cattle of any age, sex or breed are eligible for stage B payments. The rates of stage B subsidy are £9·00 for heifers and £11·25 for steers."

CHAPTER 6

SUCKLER HERDS

The majority of suckler herds have been found in hill and upland areas where they, together with sheep, have been the only means of converting upland and hill pastures into cash. Some suckler herds are also found in lowground grassland areas and occasionally herds are found on lowground arable farms. In the latter case the herd is normally used to produce cattle for fattening on the same farm, but it is common practice in the other situations to produce calves for sale after weaning in the autumn. The system of management varies according to conditions on the individual farm. Cows may be housed or run outside during winter and the herd may calve in autumn or in winter or in spring. Local practice in any one district has developed over a considerable period. The reasons for such practice may have been forgotten and indeed circumstances may well have changed. It therefore seems necessary to review here some of the factors affecting the efficiency of suckled calf production so that a system appropriate to present conditions can be selected or developed for each set of farming circumstances.

The primary objective in the management of the suckler herd is to produce calves of maximum liveweight at the time of the autumn calf sales. Moreover, the calves should be an even lot because a "tail" of lightweight calves is difficult to sell particularly in a weak market. This immediately emphasises the need to select breeding stock of the right type as discussed in Chapter 4. However, given breeding stock of any one type it will be found that the liveweight of the calf at sale time is directly related to age, the older the calf the greater the liveweight. The range in liveweight is therefore related to the length of the calving period which in turn depends on the length of the breeding period. In practice, therefore, the breeding period should not be allowed to go beyond 9 weeks but at the same time it is very desirable that all cows be settled in calf. This can only be achieved provided that the cows are rising in condition when they are served. The cow which is falling in condition either does not exhibit oestrus or does not conceive. She returns to service later and a protracted calving period must follow. In such a case the situation is often aggravated by an increased incidence of disease, especially scour, among late born calves. The disease builds up virulence during a protracted calving period and may considerably depress the growth rate achieved by late born calves, widening the range in liveweight at sale time.

Efficient production then requires that the calving period is short, that the cows produce vigorous calves of good birthweight and an ample milk supply and are rising in condition at time of service. The cows' requirements for nutrients over the year to meet these demands are indicated in Fig. 6.1 and the problem for management is to match these requirements with available feed supplies on the individual farm.

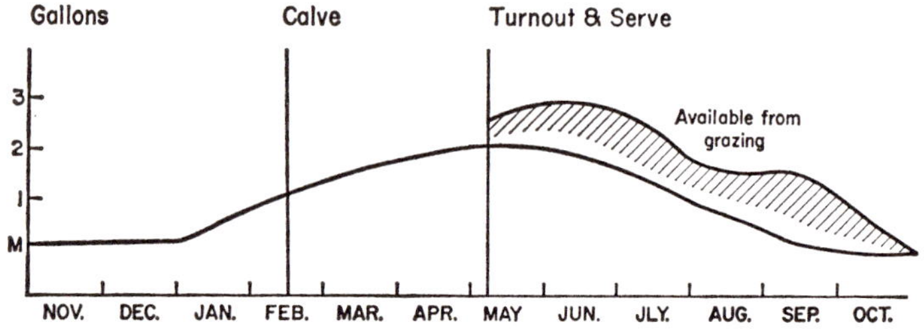

FIG. 6.1. Nutrient requirements of beef cow over year. Spring calving.

It is indicated in Fig. 6.1 that the low yielding beef cow requires feeding at around maintenance level only for 4–5 months. The nutrient requirement rises during the last 6–8 weeks before calving to the equivalent of maintenance plus 1–2 gallons of milk and continues to increase to maintenance plus 2 or 3 gallons daily during the suckling period. It is, therefore, sensible to arrange calving so that high quality feed is available during the lactation period and the dry period should coincide with any period when low quality feed is available. In this country the feed supply is ample in quantity and quality during the summer grazing period but the roughage conserved for use in winter may vary from high quality grass silage to barley straw or hay of moderate or poor quality. In the latter case it is clearly sensible to calve the herd in spring. Roughage, which may only need to be supplemented with an appropriate mineral/vitamin mixture, is fed during the winter period until 6 or 8 weeks before calving commences. The diet is then supplemented with 4 to 6 lb grain until pasture growth begins. Urea should be included in the mineral/vitamin supplement when necessary to meet the cow's requirement for protein. The breeding period coincides with maximum pasture growth which should result in an improvement in the condition of the cow, a satisfactory conception rate and subsequently a short calving period. A uniform batch of calves of satisfactory liveweight is then produced for sale. When such successful results have not been achieved a common reaction is to advance the calving date into December and January, although the poor results should properly be attributed to the type of cow used. The calves produced are then some 2 months older and this should also result in an increase in liveweight at sale time. Unfortunately, in such a case it is often found that a prolonged breeding period becomes necessary, resulting in a protracted calving period and a wide range in calf liveweights at sale time. The reasons are illustrated in Fig. 6.2. Given calving in December and January heavy

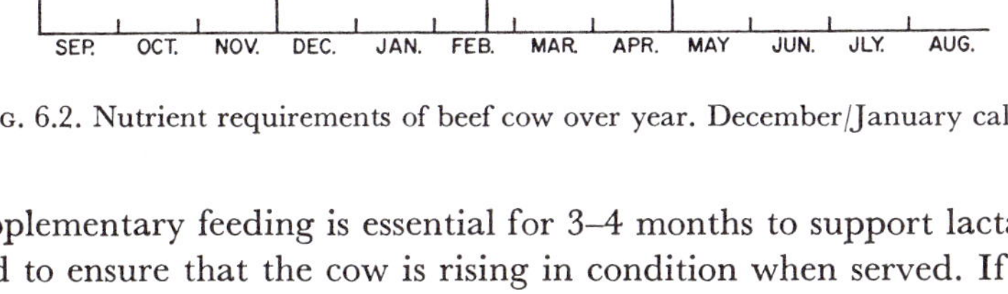

FIG. 6.2. Nutrient requirements of beef cow over year. December/January calving.

supplementary feeding is essential for 3–4 months to support lactation and to ensure that the cow is rising in condition when served. If adequate supplementary feed is not given the cow will not hold to service in March and April and prolonged breeding and calving periods must follow. Furthermore, while an even batch of calves is produced given proper supplementary feeding of the cows, it will often be found that the cost of this additional feed simply equates with the increased value of the heavier calves at sale time. Calving in December and January is therefore open to criticism since the only advantage is that the "tail" of the calves so produced may sell better in a weak market provided they are heavier than the "tail" among later born lots. In many cases it would appear to be more sound to revert to calving in February and March while effecting a change if necessary in type of cow used and applying the feeding and management methods described later for the spring calving herd.

When higher quality roughage is conserved for feeding in winter, calving in autumn can be recommended. For example, on an all grass farm where silage is made the cows must be given sufficient silage to satisfy appetite and this quantity is enough to provide for maintenance and the production of either 1 or 2 lb of liveweight gain or 1–2 gallons of milk and clearly it is sensible to have the cow in milk at this time as there seems to be little point in fattening suckler cows in winter. The herd can be calved in August and September, one advantage being a reduction in incidence in disease amongst calves. The herd may graze on foggage until November or December according to conditions and is then fed on silage sufficient to provide for the production of 2 gallons of milk. Service begins in December when the cows are still rising in condition, ensuring a short breeding period. When the herd is settled in calf feeding is maintained at the same level for the cows which may then be allowed to produce any milk above 2 gallons daily "off their backs" and any silage of inferior quality should be reserved for use during this period. The additional requirements of the calf are met by direct creep feeding of concentrates. The calves are 7–8 months of age in spring and may be weaned at or soon after being turned out. They are then rotational paddock grazed and if of the right type should be fit for slaughter at 13 to 14 months of age. The cows may be grazed on the same paddocks in tandem with, i.e. following, the calves or may be densely stocked on another pasture until mid-June. They should then be moved on to an aftermath or better pasture for 6–8 weeks before calving commences again in August. Autumn calving thus matches quality of available feed with animal requirements.

When a system appropriate to farm circumstances has been selected it is appropriate to consider details of management and feeding for the herd.

THE OUT-WINTERED HERD

The problems of feeding and management are the same whether the herd is out-wintered on either lowground or on hill and upland farms, although they may be more acute in the latter cases. Thus Welsh Black or Galloway cows may be preferred and be bred pure in extreme circumstances, but wherever possible cross-breeding and a cross-bred cow is used because cross-bred calves attract a higher price than pure bred calves. The size of the herd is largely determined by the availability and cost of winter feeding, the latter amounting to half the direct cost of producing the calves. The amount of hand feeding required varies. The cow will obtain half her maintenance requirement from grazing on a good grassy hill during an open winter, but provision should normally be made to meet the full maintenance requirement of the cow over 7 months in exposed areas and 6 months in more favourable circumstances. Hand feeding commences in the autumn or early winter when considered necessary and should err on the liberal side rather than towards underfeeding which so often is responsible for poor performance by the cow. Up to 20 lb hay daily will be required and a mineral/vitamin/urea mix should be available in boxes protected against the weather. Ideally the winter feed should be stored on the hill adjacent to a number of feeding areas offering alternative feeding sites which are used according to prevailing weather conditions. The use of only one feeding site must be avoided if possible as this may lead to poaching and the development of a heavily infected area and subsequent disease and worm troubles among the calves. Green oat sheaves may be used in lieu of hay and occasionally silage may be used. Silage is not very popular because of the additional gross weight involved. Daily transportation is difficult in winter and the tractor under load can aggravate poaching. Ideally silage pits should be sited adjacent to freely drained feeding areas. Sometimes a concrete feeding apron is provided at the pits, but these have to be very large to obviate the development of a poached area around the apron.

Concentrate feeding commences in January, 3 lb bruised barley being adequate in most cases provided that troughs can be located in a reasonably sheltered area. In some cases when the concentrate must be fed on the ground a proprietary cow cob must be used and care must be taken to ensure that such cobs carry the appropriate mineral and vitamin supplement. Concentrate feeding continues throughout calving and during the period in early spring when hypomagnesaemia may develop. It is essential that the mineral mixture contains 2 oz of calcined magnesite during the latter period. The total feed required per cow for a 180-day winter period will be at least 1·5 tons of hay or its equivalent plus 3·25 cwt barley or its equivalent.

The bulls are turned out with the herd early in May, when replacement heifers should also be introduced. When mating cannot be controlled one bull should be used per 35 cows to ensure that cows are quickly settled in calf. The provision of only one bull to 50 cows which is satisfactory when controlled mating can be practised is often not satisfactory on an open hill. The bull may be over-used, cows return to service and there may be an increase in the incidence of barren cows. If it is physically possible the bulls should be rotated, each running with the herd for 3 days only, then being withdrawn to rest. The bulls should be withdrawn at the end of a 9-week breeding period.

Creep feed should be offered to the calves from mid-August or 6 weeks before being weaned. The feed need only be bruised cereal if the calves are to be retained by the breeder, but should include 10% fishmeal if the calves are to be sold in a market where a premium is paid for bloom. This feed may not contribute to any marked increase in liveweight, but the calves suffer a reduced check when they are introduced to trough feeding during the subsequent period. The calves should be drawn into even lots for sale.

Calves should weigh 500–550 lb at sale time in early September and the herd should achieve 95 calves weaned per 100 cows put to the bull. The average life of cows in the herd should average 6–8 years.

SPRING CALVING WITH HERD HOUSED

This system is appropriate when roughage of low quality is the basis of the winter feed. The lowground arable farm where barley straw is available in quantity is an obvious example. The objective is to produce a big calf either for sale in the autumn or for fattening on the same farm. Calving must be delayed until February and March to enable the reduction of winter feed costs to a minimum and this again emphasises the importance of type of cow and sire as discussed in Chapter 4. The Hereford Friesian cow is an obvious choice, producing vigorous calves of good birthweight and growth potential which can be fully expressed as the dam offers an ample supply of milk. Furthermore, this cross is available in large numbers. The sire used should have a recorded 400-day weight exceeding 1100 lb and he should be lean rather than fat at that liveweight.

The cows are housed before grass supplies fail, which means by 1 November in the north. They should be sub-divided into groups of 10 according to anticipated calving date to permit proper management. Barley straw is fed to appetite supplemented by feed which offers the lowest cost units of energy and protein in the particular area. Supplements which have given satisfactory results are 30 lb wet distillers grains, OR 15 lb wet distillers grains plus 3 lb barley, OR 6 lb barley plus 68 g urea. In all cases a mineral/vitamin supplement must also be used and this can be purchased pre-mixed with urea when urea is required in the diet. Daily consumption of straw per head with the above supplements is about 16 lb, 18 lb and 26 lb respectively. This feeding level provides for maintenance only, but it has been established that the Hereford Friesian when housed in good condition produces a satisfactory calf and milk supply without further supplementation. Winter feed costs are therefore very much reduced. These diets are prone to induce muscular dystrophy in calves. Veterinary advice should therefore be taken regarding treatment with either vitamin E or selenium. Cows and calves are turned out to graze in late April and require $\frac{2}{3}$ of an acre of grass per cow and calf for the full grazing season. The grass acreage is divided into 8–10 paddocks which are grazed in rotation. As soon as the calves begin to learn to leave their dams a creep should be provided leading into the next paddock, giving the calves first access to each paddock in turn. Total nitrogen usage need not exceed 160 units per acre.

The breeding period should be restricted to 1 May to 7 July and if the herd numbers more than 35 cows bulls should be used singly and in rotation. The calves can be weaned very simply and effectively by closing the calf creep when all the calves are in the forward paddock. Cows and calves then lie on either side of the fence and after 2 or 3 days the calves are moved forward, leaving the cows in their original paddock. The calves may then be moved to another field or may be housed a few days later. This system works well presumably because separation is initially incomplete and no breaking out by either the cows or calves has been experienced. The calves should weigh 500–550 lb in late September.

This system has been successfully used to produce one weaned calf on $\frac{2}{3}$ of an acre of grass. The grazing requirement could easily be reduced to $\frac{1}{2}$ an acre given very mild intensification. Where the calf is to be fattened on the same farm, silage made from the other $\frac{1}{2}$ acre supplemented by barley makes possible the production, rearing and finishing of one fat animal per forage acre per year. There seems to be no good reason why this system should not be developed and widely adopted in grain producing areas.

BREEDING COW SUBSIDIES

According to the type of herd, one of the following subsidies is attracted by the suckler cow:

Beef Cow Subsidy

Cows maintained throughout the year in regular herds kept primarily for breeding calves for beef are eligible for subsidy at the rate of £11 per head. The subsidy is not payable if the cow qualifies for hill cow subsidy. For payment purposes the maximum stocking rate is one cow per 2 acres.

Hill Cow Subsidy

Cows maintained throughout the year in regular breeding herds kept on eligible hill land, for the purpose of breeding store cattle for sale, are eligible for subsidy at the rate of £18·75 per head in 1971/2. In addition, a winter keep supplement of £5 per head will be paid for every animal qualifying for the subsidy in 1971/2. The subsidy is not payable if the cow qualifies for beef cow subsidy. For payment purposes the maximum stocking ratio is one cow per 4 acres of hill land.

CHAPTER 7

THE SEMI-INTENSIVE OR EIGHTEEN-MONTH SYSTEM

THIS system of beef production was developed during the 1950s as a method of utilising male calves born in the National Dairy Herd and which previously were commonly slaughtered at birth. Autumn born beef cross dairy calves are most commonly used, being available in large numbers because the dairyman often uses a beef bull on his heifers which are served to calve in the autumn as a means of ensuring the production of a high proportion of milk at winter prices.

The objective is to produce a finished animal of 1000 lb liveweight at 18 months of age or less. Assuming a birth weight of 80 lb, this implies the achievement of an average liveweight gain of 1·67 lb daily from birth to slaughter and in practice this involves achieving an average gain of 2 lb daily when possible to counteract the loss in liveweight which may be suffered for a period after turnout and housing. This rate of liveweight gain can only be achieved if the best possible practice is followed.

Once again the type of animal rather than breed is important. Pure bred Friesians or calves out of Ayrshire and Friesian cows and sired by beef bulls with good 400-day weight records should be sought for purchase at not less than 4 days of age, thus ensuring that they have received their dam's colostrum. Calves born before the end of October are to be preferred because ultimately they tend to be more profitable than later born calves. For a variety of reasons the latter take longer to finish during the second winter when feed costs are high.

FIRST WINTER

The objective during the first winter period is to grow the calf to a liveweight of at least 400 lb before it is turned out to graze in the following spring. This target is more readily achieved starting with calves born in September and October rather than later. Calves born in early autumn are weaned and the rumen is fully functional before the onset of cold weather. Heat of fermentation produced in the rumen assists in the maintenance of body temperature and the calf is less dependent on its environment. On the other hand, calves born from November onwards must go through the pre-ruminant stage during cold weather and depend more heavily on good stockmanship and well-insulated buildings. They are more prone to suffer from scour and pneumonia. Furthermore, late born calves just do not have time to reach 400 lb liveweight at turnout even if they achieve the same rate of liveweight gain as earlier born calves. This is illustrated in Table 7.1, which shows the liveweight at turnout on 1 May for calves bought at 80 lb liveweight from September to December and assuming they gain 1·43 lb daily to 12 weeks of age and subsequently 2 lb daily to turnout.

TABLE 7.1
LIVEWEIGHT OF AUTUMN-BORN CALVES AT TURNOUT

80 lb calf bought	200 lb liveweight on	Liveweight on 1 May
1 Sept.	24 Nov.	512
1 Oct.	24 Dec.	466
1 Nov.	25 Jan.	390
1 Dec.	24 Feb.	330

The calves are reared on either the twice daily or once daily bucket feeding systems described in Chapter 5. A flakey palatable concentrate is offered to appetite to encourage consumption, early rumen development and the attainment of 200 lb liveweight at 12 weeks of age. When concentrate intake reaches 6 lb per head daily the mixture is changed to 85% cereal with 15% earthnut cake and silage is introduced together with swedes if available. The intake of silage and swedes is allowed to increase with appetite and reaches 15–20 lb daily by turnout depending on the birth date of the calves and on the quality of the silage. If silage alone is available, intake should reach 20–26 lb daily by turnout. The silage used should be leafy, the dry matter percentage 20–25%, the crude protein in the dry matter 14–16% and the Starch Equivalent of the fresh material 12–14%.

The calves should be vaccinated against hoose (lungworm) before being turned out if there is any record of hoose occurring on the farm.

TURNOUT

Every effort must be made to ensure that calves reach 400 lb liveweight before being turned out because performance on grass is related to liveweight at turnout, heavier calves making better liveweight gains. Recording results have confirmed this and reveal that calves weighing over 400 lb at turnout gain on average 0·2 lb more daily during the grazing season than calves which weigh less than 400 lb at turnout. It would appear that the digestive tract is not sufficiently developed in lighter calves and they are not capable of ingesting sufficient grass to enable them to grow to their full potential. The situation is aggravated in wet weather when the dry matter percentage in the grass is reduced and the calf has also to ingest a considerable amount of superficial moisture on the grass.

Turnout should be a gradual process so that the calves do not suffer an abrupt change in diet and environment. A full feed should be offered before the calves are turned out each morning, the period spent at grass increasing daily until it is reasonably certain that night time temperatures will not be low. The calves are then left out at night. These steps can only be readily put into practice either when a pasture is available close to the steading or when a shed is available in the pasture to be used. An old permanent pasture adjacent to the steading and heavily infested with worms *must not be used*. Hay should be available in the field during the turnout period and when turnout is completed 2 lb grain should be fed daily so long as it is consumed. The feeding of concentrates throughout the grazing period is debatable. It may not be necessary when ideal circumstances prevail, but these include the provision of short leafy high dry matter grass throughout the summer and the absence of cold wet nights. In many areas the dry matter content of the sward fluctuates widely, often falling well below 20% during a normal British summer, and the quality of the sward tends to decline in late summer even when the standard of grazing management is high. M.L.C. survey results show that the average daily liveweight gain is 0·2 lb higher when 2 lb grain is fed daily from June to housing. This level of supplementation is necessary for 3–4 weeks after turnout partly to reduce abruptness in change of diet and as a carrier for calcined magnesite when this is necessary. It therefore seems reasonable to feed this supplement throughout the grazing season except in areas favoured with very good weather and provided grazing management is of a high order.

GRAZING MANAGEMENT

The objective is to offer short leafy grass to the cattle throughout the grazing period. This is very difficult to achieve with set stocking and entails the adoption of some form of rotational paddock grazing. The field should not have been grazed by cattle during the previous 12 months. If available, a field which carried a forward creep grazed flock of ewes and lambs during the previous summer is ideal. The sward is then close and dense and fencing costs are spread over two enterprises and years. A minimum of eight paddocks is desirable, each being grazed for 3–5 days as appropriate. It is essential that the cattle return to the first paddock to be grazed when it is again ready for grazing, any paddocks which are bypassed being cut for silage. This will usually occur during the first and maybe second rotations and the grazing cycle will vary from 21 to 30 days during the season. Phosphate and potash should be applied as required during the previous autumn. Nitrogen is applied in March/April at 80 units per acre and this dressing may be staggered round the paddocks to encourage the development of growth in rotation. Subsequently each paddock should receive 40 units of nitrogen after each grazing or 80 units after being cut for silage. Applications should cease in late July or early August.

If sward recovery is slow because of drought, care must be taken not to accelerate the progression of the cattle round the paddocks. They must be held in each paddock for 3 days, cereal being fed as necessary. Rapid progression round the paddocks only aggravates the grass shortage if the sward is not given time to recover. In such a situation the cattle may be moved to graze silage aftermath if available and these should be rotationally grazed. Such a change on to a clean sward may also be desirable in late July as a means of combating a build-up of worm infestation on the initial grazing area from which a late cut can be taken for conservation. All paddocks should be topped if necessary after each grazing to prevent a build-up of stemmy material in the sward which would depress intake of digestible nutrients as the season progresses. The area allocated to grazing should be stocked at the rate of at least three animals per acre, i.e. over the full grazing season, to ensure that paddocks are fully grazed. If a lower stocking rate is used excessive topping will be required to ensure that there is not a build-up of indigestible stemmy material in the sward. Good grazing management permits stocking at the rate of four animals per acre and this can be achieved without depressing individual animal performance.

In early September consideration must be given to housing, which must take place before the onset of cold nights, which will be not later than 1 October in the north. If supplementary feeding has been stopped during the grazing season, feeding of 2–3 lb grain daily should recommence some 2–3 weeks before housing and in areas where swedes are used a load should be spread in the field a week before housing.

THE FINISHING PERIOD

At housing the cattle should be evenly grouped according to sex, size, condition and horned or polled. They should be penned if possible in groups of 10 to 12, the smaller the number per pen the easier the management, it being easier to spot the sick animal, the poor doer and the bully. It is difficult to ensure that a "tail" of poor doers does not develop when a group of say 50 animals is penned together. Care must be taken to ensure that adequate ventilation is provided to reduce undue sweating at night especially for the first 2 weeks after housing.

The old-fashioned practice of clipping cattle along the backbone is to be commended. It may be difficult to prove a direct monetary return but when practised provides evidence of stockmanship. The stockman must be given time to develop and apply his skill. There is a strong tendency to overlook this point, to emphasise only output per man-hour and develop units in which the objective is to put the stockman in charge of the maximum number of animals. Such action is undoubtedly necessary, but note must be taken of the need for the stockman to "know" his animals and what is now being called "job satisfaction". The satisfied stockman is more likely to look to points of management than the man who is disgruntled because he is over-stressed and can never catch up with his work. Observation and experience show indeed that the good stockman has time to "talk" to and handle his animals. Such practice encourages the development of docility and, surely, improved performance.

Feeding during the finishing period is commonly based on grass silage and barley. Intake of silage varies with quality when it is self fed or trough fed to appetite reaching 12, 10 and 8 lb per live hundred-weight per day when silage quality is good, average and poor respectively. The daily ration of barley must therefore be adjusted according to silage quality to maintain the objective of 2 lb daily live-weight gain. Daily barley requirements are calculated in Table 7.2 for cattle rising from 700 to 900 lb liveweight, assuming that silage is initially fed to appetite.

TABLE 7.2
DAILY BARLEY REQUIREMENT TO MAINTAIN 2 LB DAILY GAIN

Silage				lb barley to raise S.E. intake to	
Quality	S.E. fresh	Intake (lb)	Intake S.E. (lb)	8·6 lb at 700 lb liveweight	10·2 lb at 900 lb liveweight
Good	12	72	8·64	0	2
Average	10	60	6·00	4	6
Poor	8	48	3·84	7	9

It is clear that barley requirement is inversely proportional to silage quality, but a point which is often overlooked is the parallel fact that the higher the quality the greater the tonnage required per head if the silage is fed to appetite. The point is made in Table 7.3.

TABLE 7.3
SILAGE REQUIREMENTS

lb/day	tons/head 150 days	tons/50 head 150 days
72	4·8	240
60	4·0	200
48	3·2	160

If these facts are not appreciated, the silage pit may well be empty before a group of cattle is finished for slaughter. In practice it is more sound to calculate the daily silage allowance from the tonnage available and to adjust barley intake accordingly. The daily barley requirements would then be as shown in Table 7.4, given 50 lb silage available per head per day.

TABLE 7.4
BARLEY REQUIRED TO MAINTAIN 2 LB DAILY GAIN WITH 50 LB SILAGE FED

S.E. silage	lb barley to raise S.E. intake to	
	8·6 lb at 700 lb liveweight	10·2 lb at 900 lb liveweight
12	4	6
10	5	7
8	7	9

Every effort must be made to produce silage of high quality as a means of reducing food costs. First, high-quality silage provides a lower S.E. Unit Cost than low quality silage (see p. 17). Second, the amount of barley required is reduced and indeed survey results indicate that winter fattening can only be economic when high quality roughages are used.

The rations given in Table 7.4 are all successfully used and can be amended to include feeds such as swedes, beet pulp, potatoes and wet grains when these feeds are available at appropriate S.E. Unit Prices.

Animals must be sent to slaughter as soon as they carry sufficient condition and when the rate of liveweight gain falls below 2 lb daily. The food cost per lb of gain increases rapidly beyond this stage and care must be taken not to over-fatten cattle which results only in additional food costs and a reduction in profit margins. Particular care must be taken with animals of early maturing type, which should be fit to slaughter at about 900 lb liveweight. Animals sired by bulls of satisfactory 400-day weight should grow to 1000 or 1100 lb liveweight before they must be slaughtered.

This system has now been practised for a number of years. Practice followed successfully at Craibstone, The North of Scotland College of Agriculture farm near Aberdeen, is summarised as follows:

Birth to turning out—

Up to 25 gal whole milk

Up to 55 gal good milk substitute

Concentrates and hay from 1 week

Weaned when eating 2½ lb concentrates

Silage and swedes offered soon after 12 weeks of age, 15–20 lb of each being fed daily before calves are turned out. Concentrates held at maximum of 6 lb daily. Calves turned out gradually weighing over 400 lb.

Grazing period—

2 lb oats or barley fed daily throughout.

Finishing period—

Swedes rising to 40 lb daily

Silage rising to 40 lb daily

Distiller's grains (wet) 10 lb daily

Oats and/or barley 4–6 lb daily

The mean performance data for seven groups of beef × Ayrshire animals are given in Table 7.5.

TABLE 7.5

MEAN PERFORMANCE DATA: AUTUMN BORN STEERS OUT OF AYRSHIRE COWS

Sire	Year born	No.	Liveweight (lb) at				Age at slaughter (days)
			Collection	Turnout	Housing	Slaughter	
Beef Shorthorn	1960	23	84	417	612	934	529
Aberdeen Angus	1961	38	74	343	558	910	515
Beef Shorthorn	1962	15	67	480	655	928	538
Hereford	1962	12	89	490	700	1016	546
Beef Shorthorn	1963	10	83	444	671	976	533
Charolais	1963	12	89	489	745	1122	585
Hereford	1964	32	112	416	690	975	531

Cutting-up data for the 1963 Beef Shorthorn and Charolais × Steers are given in Table 2.1 on p. 10.

During recent years the food costs associated with this system have been approximately £20 for the calf rearing winter, £5 for the grazing season and £20 for the final winter. This has left a margin above food costs of £35–£42. All foods were produced on the farm except milk substitute, the protein supplement used in the calf concentrate and wet grains and represent the produce of about 1·3 acres.

CHAPTER 8

INTENSIVE OR TWELVE-MONTH SYSTEMS

I. ALL CONCENTRATE OR BARLEY BEEF

During the 1950s the semi-intensive system of beef production described in Chapter 7 developed and its adoption led to a gradual reduction in the average age of cattle at slaughter. The advantage of quicker turnover was thus achieved as more cattle were killed at about 18 months of age. Further success was reached in this direction as the "All Concentrate System" was developed during the 1960s, when it was demonstrated that animals of suitable type could be fed to reach slaughter condition at 10–12 months of age.

The development of this system has produced many repercussions and maybe the most important is that it definitely removes at least this system of beef production from the lowly scavenging role suffered when beef production had to make do with the residue of management time and skill remaining after more important cash crop enterprises had been dealt with. The system makes possible the development of a self-contained unit, very intensive in operation and requiring a high degree of management skill. It may also suffer all the difficulties of intensivism far removed from those associated with dog and stick farming of beef on extensive pastures.

ADVANTAGES

Many advantages are claimed for this system. Above all it is basically simple steer calves being fed to achieve 200 to 220 lb liveweight at 12 weeks of age and subsequently feeding to appetite on an all concentrate diet reaching slaughter condition at 800 to 900 lb liveweight and at 10–12 months of age. The animals are never turned out to graze and thus avoid the checks to growth associated with turnout and housing. The labour requirement for feeding is low, since self-feeding is practised. Time is only required for the topping up of hoppers or troughs and this can be done when labour is available and is not necessary at fixed times. Feed distribution can indeed be fully automated. Because of the low labour requirement the system lends itself readily for inclusion on a dairy farm where home-bred steer calves can be taken through to slaughter without creating a demand for extra labour. The dairy farmer can thus acquire an additional enterprise at minimum extra cost. At another extreme it is possible to develop a large unit provided that the difficulties associated with scale of enterprise can be overcome.

The carcase produced possesses many attributes, outstanding among these being extreme tenderness which is obviously related to the age of 10 or 12 months at slaughter. A minimum of fat trimming is required and the 450–500 lb carcase is readily cut into small lean joints which are very suitable for the prepack supermarket trade. Further, carcases are relatively uniform because the feeding system, slaughter weight and age at slaughter are uniform wherever the system is practised. A fair degree of repeatability in weight and quality of carcase thus becomes available to the butcher, a quality which has previously been markedly lacking in beef markets.

When first introduced, a net profit of £20 to £25 per head was claimed which together with the above advantages attracted many to adopt this system of beef production.

Finally, from the national viewpoint the system assists in the utilisation of dairy bred calves for beef production.

DIFFICULTIES

Any such list of advantages must be considered together with associated disadvantages or difficulties which include the following: in the first place the profit margin realised depends basically on the relationship between the price realised for beef on the one hand and on the other the costs of calves and barley together with growth rate, food conversion and hence food costs per pound of liveweight gain achieved. The price realised by beef remains relatively constant so the margin shrinks if calf and barley prices rise. It is necessary to arrange a supply of calves for the full year and it is difficult to forecast spring and pre-harvest barley prices which rise if barley is then in short supply. If the feeder has to buy at this time the profit margin is reduced. It is not easy to arrange a regular supply of suitable calves particularly for the bigger unit. This is even more difficult when calves are taken in at 12 weeks of age because contracts with calf rearing units often break down.

The development of a big unit may encounter difficulties in obtaining planning permission for buildings which may be rated, in arranging the disposal of the large quantities of dung or slurry produced and in providing adequate ventilation.

Although the labour requirement for feeding is low, a high degree of stockmanship is required. Frequent inspection is necessary to ensure that adequate ventilation is provided to restrict outbreaks of respiratory disorders and to cope with bloating which may occur.

Finally, the butcher may object because of the high proportion of abscessed livers which have to be condemned and some consumers do not care for the meat if it is lacking in flavour.

After some 10 years of development a balance has been achieved between these advantages and difficulties and currently some 10% of our beef supplies are produced by this system.

THE SYSTEM

Friesian bull calves are reared on milk and milk substitute fed either once or twice per day as described on pp. 42–44. Hay is offered and concentrates are fed to appetite. At 200 to 220 lb liveweight the feed is gradually changed to the fattening mix consisting of 85% barley and 15% of a supplement which includes minerals, vitamins and protein to ensure a crude protein level of 14% in the mix. Two supplements which are widely used are detailed in Table 8.1. (See page 70.)

Both are equally efficient, but the urea supplement is currently cheaper. It must be emphasised that urea must not be fed before calves are fully ruminant and this is ensured by introduction at 200–220 lb liveweight. Very careful mixing is essential to ensure even distribution of urea through the supplement, if this is mixed on the farm. If this cannot be guaranteed, a proprietary supplement should be used.

Concentrates are fed to appetite and care must be taken to ensure that feed is always available in troughs or self-feed hoppers. If the hoppers are allowed by mistake to empty, some animals will almost certainly gorge themselves when the hoppers are refilled and bloating will follow.

TABLE 8.1
PROTEIN AND UREA SUPPLEMENTS FOR INCLUSION IN BARLEY BEEF MIX

	Protein supplement %	Urea supplement %
Ground barley	26·9	78·8
Soya bean meal	60·0	—
Urea	—	6·7
Limestone	8·7	7·7
Steamed bone flour	2·8	4·4
Salt	1·7	1·7
Vitamin A	42 million I.U.*	
Vitamin D	10 million I.U.*	
C.P. % in D.M.	34	

* Per ton of supplement.

It is preferable that the barley be bruised or crimped rather than hammer milled. This is because it is important to retain fibre in the husk in the long form, thus reducing the incidence of bloat. Moist grain can be used with advantage, being very palatable and reducing the amount of dust in the feed. This in turn helps to restrict the incidence of respiratory disorders in the cattle.

Straw should be made available as an insurance against bloat if the cattle are housed on slatted floors. Rate of liveweight gain and food conversion efficiency are not depressed so long as straw intake does not exceed 1–2 lb daily. The feeding of straw is not necessary if used as bedding and provided that the pens are littered regularly.

It is generally recommended that the steers be implanted under the skin on the back of the ear with 60 mg hexoestrol at 550 lb liveweight. This treatment leads to an improvement of about 13% in food conversion efficiency. Single implantation produces as good results as implanting 30 mg at 440 lb and again at 660 lb liveweight. Before adopting this practice producers should ensure that there is no trade resistance in their market against implanted cattle.

At 550 lb liveweight the crude protein content of the diet can fall to 11% and it follows that there is no need then for the inclusion of the protein supplement provided that the crude protein content of the barley is 11% or more. The crude protein level in barley can vary from 6 to 14%. It is therefore necessary to analyse each batch of barley so that the protein supplement may be omitted or included at an appropriate reduced level, from 550 lb liveweight to slaughter. It must not be forgotten that supplementation with minerals and vitamins is still required if the protein supplement is omitted. A suitable mineral vitamin mix for inclusion with barley of 11% crude protein is given in Table 8.2.

TABLE 8.2
MINERAL/VITAMIN SUPPLEMENT FOR INCLUSION WITH 11% C.P. BARLEY FROM 550 LB LIVEWEIGHT TO SLAUGHTER

Barley meal	48·0%
Ground limestone	26·0%
Steamed bone flour	15·0%
Salt	5·0%
Liquid paraffin	6·0%
Vitamin A	120 million I.U.
Vitamin D	30 million I.U.
Rate of inclusion in diet	5%

Animals should be marketed as soon as an acceptable degree of finish is achieved; this will be from 10 months of age and 800 lb liveweight onward depending on breed and type of animal. Feed conversion efficiency falls and food cost per pound of gain rises rapidly beyond this point so care must be taken to avoid overfattening stock.

The results obtained when this system is practised are illustrated in Table 8.3, which summarises the findings of one M.L.C. survey involving 5361 animals fed in 263 groups.

TABLE 8.3
RESULTS FROM INTENSIVE CEREAL BEEF ENTERPRISES

Daily liveweight gain (lb)		Feed conversion efficiency (lb/lb)		Feed cost/lb L.W.G.	
Avge.	Group range	Avge.	Group range	Avge.	Group range
2·4	1·6–3·8	5·9	3·6–10·4	7p	4½–30½p

Note must be taken of the wide range in results and every effort must be made to obtain results which are above the averages given in Table 8.3. Consideration must therefore now be given to factors affecting success in this direction.

The type of animal is important in that the animal is required to gain more than 2·5 lb daily, lay down the minimum of fat and hence achieve a low food conversion ratio. Friesian, Charolais/Friesian and Hereford/Friesian steers are most successful and should be bought provided that calf costs are not excessive. Earlier maturing types such as the pure bred Ayrshire are on average incapable of gaining weight as rapidly as the Friesian but can be used successfully when they can be bought at £15 less than pure Friesian calves.

The feeding method recommended is to feed to appetite, but some producers have practised the introduction of restriction of feed intake at levels varying between 16 and 20 lb per head daily. Some claim that this has not led to a depression of rate of liveweight gain and have therefore found an improvement in food conversion efficiency. However, a depression in rate of gain has been recorded in most cases and this implies that restriction of feed level requires careful examination before it can be recommended. The search is not simply for a crude feed restriction level but rather for the optimum nutrient intake level at which lean meat development continues without excessive fat deposition. Some evidence indicates that this may be achieved by feeding the animal to appetite to 550 lb liveweight on an all concentrate mix of Starch Equivalent 80 in the dry matter. The feed is then changed to a mix of lower cost and of reduced energy concentration having a Starch Equivalent of 70 in the dry matter. This mix also is fed to appetite. A mixture of one part barley to one part wet distiller's grains supplemented with minerals and vitamins has been successfully used to reduce feed costs in this way. The successful development of such a pattern of feeding would lead to a reduction in food costs per pound of liveweight gain.

Food costs are of vital importance and the Unit Cost Method described on pp. 15–18 must be used. There is no evidence which proves that feeds of high price per ton produce any better results than low cost feeds, always provided of course that the feeds used are suitable for the system. Thus, one survey showed that mixes costing less than £24 per ton produced the same liveweight gain results as others costing over £28 per ton. Clearly there is no point in using expensive feed when no benefits accrue.

ALTERNATIVES TO BARLEY

Barley has been the cereal most commonly used in the United Kingdom in all concentrate feeding because it has offered the lowest cost Starch Equivalent Unit. Occasionally other feeds, including wheat, maize and beet pulp, may compete with barley on this basis and should then be used. Bruised wheat and cracked maize can each be included up to the 50% level in the mix, but 15% oats should then also be added to maintain the fibre content at the desired level to minimise bloat. Dried beet pulp has been successfully used incorporated initially at low levels and rising to 30% in the mix.

COST OF OVERFATTENING

The need to avoid overfattening is repeatedly stressed and is again mentioned because it has such a marked effect on profitability. This relationship has been very clearly demonstrated with referencc to all concentrate feeding because it has been possible to record liveweight gain and feed intake in a large number of units. Some results are given in Table 8.4. (See page 74.)

These figures show that the food cost per pound liveweight gain rises rapidly as Friesian steers pass 800 lb liveweight, this being due to an increase in fat deposition and a reduction in feed conversion efficiency. They also show that feed costs begin to exceed the return of 10p per lb liveweight currently realised, at about 900 lb liveweight. Animals must therefore be slaughtered before this point is passed.

TABLE 8.4
PERFORMANCE OF INTENSIVELY FED CATTLE OVER 800 LB LIVEWEIGHT

Weight of cattle (lb)	No. of cattle	Average daily liveweight gain (lb)	Average feed conversion ratio (lb per lb)	Average feed consumption (lb)	Average feed cost per lb liveweight gain (p)
		Friesian steers			
800–849	359	2·1	8·1	17·1	8
850–899	325	2·1	9·0	18·8	9
900 plus	268	2·0	10·3	20·0	10

MORTALITY

Profitability can also be grossly affected by mortality level, heavy losses being suffered in some units when the system was first introduced. Such heavy losses are usually caused by bloating and severe outbreaks of virus pneumonia. Bloat is now largely avoided, care being taken to ensure that fibre intake is maintained at a satisfactory level and the average mortality level should not exceed 2–3% from 220 lb liveweight to slaughter. When this level is exceeded it is usually due to outbreaks of virus pneumonia which can be difficult to control in large units. The presence of sub-clinical virus pneumonia is probably responsible for the seasonal variations in performance which are recorded in nearly all units, liveweight gain reaching a maximum level during the summer months and falling to a low level in mid-winter.

YOUNG BULLS

The use of young bulls in the All Concentrate Feeding System was proposed in the early 1960s, not long after this system developed. As noted above, the implantation of steers with the synthetic growth promoting hormone hexoestrol was and still is recommended. A natural development was to suggest that the bull calf should be left entire, thus permitting it to utilise the naturally produced growth-promoting hormone testosterone. It is argued that the conventional reasons for castration, i.e. to eliminate indiscriminate breeding and to improve docility, are obviated since the All Concentrate fed animal is housed from birth to slaughter. Furthermore, it is claimed that unacceptable "bull taint" is not a problem because the animals are slaughtered when young and before this taint develops. The advantages to be gained are well established. Compared with the castrate, the young bull shows an improvement of 10–15% in food conversion efficiency, of 10% in growth rate and yields some 3–7% more lean meat in the carcase.

The practice is now permitted, but producers have to obtain a permit from the Ministry of Agriculture (Department of Agriculture in Scotland). A permit must be obtained in respect of each bull before it reaches the age of 10 months. Premises are inspected and must provide secure housing and permit feeding to be done from the outside of pens. Safe handling facilities must also be available. A guarantee must be given that the bull will not be used for breeding.

Young bulls are not eligible for live certification for calf subsidy at Stage A (see p. 47) or for liveweight certification for the fatstock guaranteed price. They must be presented for certification on a deadweight basis at an approved centre, application forms for fatstock guarantee and calf subsidy having been submitted in advance. The bull must not have cut any permanent incisor teeth and the carcase must conform to the standard summarised on p. 12. *If the carcase fails to be certified for guarantee payment it also fails to attract calf subsidy.* Failure to meet the qualifying standards is most likely to occur when slaughter is delayed, since this may lead to the development of darker coarse textured flesh and of heavy forequarters. "Young bulls" should therefore be slaughtered at an early age, but care must be taken to ensure that they carry sufficient "finish" to ensure that the carcase will qualify.

The number of young bulls slaughtered has increased gradually but has only reached some 3000 annually. Producers who have adopted the practice claim that the amount of paperwork involved is unduly excessive and strive to have this reduced.

The decision whether or not to use young bulls must be made by the individual producer who has to balance the difficulties of additional paperwork and above all the provision of safe working facilities for his men against the additional return to be expected.

HIGH FIBRE CHANGE OVER DIET

Occasionally a producer may decide to introduce older cattle into an All Concentrate unit. The previous dietary history of the animals may be unknown or they may have been grazing or receiving a roughage based diet. In this event very severe bloating and deaths may occur if the change in diet is abrupt. A gradual change in diet from roughage to all concentrate must be achieved. A high fibre mix of the type given in Table 8.5 should be introduced and increased until it is eaten to appetite after 7–10 days, when the high fibre mix in turn is gradually replaced over the following 7 days by the normal fattening mix.

TABLE 8.5
HIGH FIBRE DIET FOR TRANSITION PERIOD FROM ROUGHAGE TO ALL CONCENTRATE DIET

	%
Rolled barley	24
Rolled oats	25
Oat husks	25
Undecorticated cotton cake	25
Dicalcium phosphate	1

II. USING WEANED SUCKLED CALVES

It has been conventional practice to wean suckled calves at 6–8 months of age and then to rear the animals on for 2 or $2\frac{1}{2}$ years before slaughtering them either off grass at $2\frac{1}{2}$ years of age or at 3 years of age in late winter or spring, having been fattened inside. Age at slaughter has been reduced during the last 20 years and the stage is now being reached where many weaned calves are slaughtered at 12–16 months of age. This system of beef production can therefore be just as intensive as the All Concentrate system in terms of speed of turnover. The calves are housed in autumn soon after being weaned and are fed to appetite on hay or silage together with cereal grain at an appropriate level. This method of feeding has exposed the disadvantage of the extremely early maturing type of animal in that it reaches slaughter condition at light weights and becomes grossly overfat if fed on to achieve greater liveweight before being slaughtered. Furthermore, many animals of this type are only capable of gaining at the rate of 1·5–1·75 lb daily even when fed to appetite. The situation has been aggravated by the fact that animals of this type have commanded high prices at weaned calf sales. The margin between buying and selling prices realised over the fattening period is therefore small and may not even cover food costs. Beef producers who are developing this system are therefore seeking a more late maturing type of calf which possesses a better potential for liveweight gain. The point is illustrated in the results given in Table 8.6 for two lots of weaned calves. One lot were out of Hereford/Friesian dams and were sired by a Lincoln Red bull which was selected partly on the basis of a good 400-day liveweight. The second lot were sired by an Aberdeen Angus bull selected on conventional standards and were out of cross-bred beef cows. Both lots were housed after weaning and the fattening ration consisted of swedes and grass silage which were fed to appetite plus distiller's wet grains and barley grain. The maximum daily food intake achieved per head was 5 lb barley, 7 lb wet grains, 25 lb swedes and 25 lb silage.

TABLE 8.6
SUCKLED STEER CALVES. PERFORMANCE OVER FATTENING PERIOD

	Lincoln Red × Hereford/Friesian	Aberdeen Angus × Cross-bred Beef Cow
Liveweight at housing (lb)	555	635
Liveweight at slaughter (lb)	905	835
Age at slaughter (days)	384	423
Carcase weight (lb)	526	491
Daily gain housing to slaughter (lb)	1·87	1·71
Liveweight/day of age at slaughter (lb)	2·36	1·98
Carcase weight/day of age (lb)	1·37	1·16
Killing out (%)	58·1	58·8
Margin selling–buying price	£36·58	£13·01
Cost of feed*	£23·39	£11·87
Margin over feed cost+purchase price	£13·19	£1·14

* Feeds charged to cattle at Barley £22, Wet Grains £3·50, Silage £3·50 and Swedes £4·50, all per ton.

The calves sired by the Aberdeen Angus bull and out of beef cows were of superb type by conventional standards but they had to be slaughtered after a 115-day fattening period. The later maturing Lincoln Red × Hereford/Friesian calves were fed for 188 days before it was necessary to slaughter them. The animals were less than 13 months of age at slaughter and the margin over feed cost plus purchase price was sufficient to leave direct profit, which was not the case for the group of early maturing type calves. The implication is clear. When fattening weaned calves either buy calves of an appropriate late maturing type or breed them as described on pp. 55–56, noting that in the latter case a feasible target is to breed, rear and fatten one animal per forage acre per year.

CHAPTER 9

CONVENTIONAL FATTENING IN WINTER AND IN SUMMER

BUYING STORE CATTLE

The systems of beef production described in Chapters 7, 8 and 9 are being widely practised, but large numbers of animals still follow a more traditional route from birth to slaughter and many so-called "store" cattle are bought in the autumn and spring for fattening inside and on the grass respectively. The possibility of making a direct profit from these enterprises depends initially on the farmer's skill as a buyer of cattle. This skill may only be developed after personal and maybe bitter experience because the requirements cannot be fully learned in a classroom.

The buyer must be a good judge of stock and be able to recognise signs of both good and ill health. He looks for an animal with a slack, supple skin as being indicative of good health and avoids one with a tight skin and harsh staring coat, which may be due to a sluggish blood supply. The eye should be placid, indicating a mild temperament. The animal with a fiery eye or showing signs of a nervous disposition is avoided. The pot-bellied animal is avoided because it will yield a high proportion of offal on slaughter and butcher buyers will not bid freely if the animal is sold in the live market. Above all the buyer must learn to recognise the animal's potential for further liveweight gain. Experience may indicate that animals reared in specific areas or on individual farms excel in this quality and will therefore be sought. In addition to these points which contribute to the art of buying, regard must be made to the relationship between buying price and anticipated fat price, i.e. at slaughter.

First with reference to cattle bought for winter fattening, the purchase price per live hundredweight should be less than the anticipated fat price because the value of the increase in liveweight obtained usually equates with the food costs incurred. The following figures could apply to an animal bought on 1 October and fed to gain 2 lb daily over 140 days and sold fat on 18 February.

1 October	7 cwt at £10/cwt	Purchase price	£70
18 February	9½ cwt at £10/cwt	Fat price	£95
"Feeder's margin"			£25
Food cost	20 weeks at £1·25/week		£25
To cover all other costs and profit			0

In other words, the chance of making direct profit is very slender unless there is an increase in the value of the unit of liveweight during the fattening period. This is largely related to the high food costs incurred in winter feeding. Food costs during the grazing period are lower and because of this it is possible to make a direct profit on fattening even when the buying price exceeds the fat price realised by £1 to £2 per cwt. The figures for an animal grazed for 20 weeks from 1 May to 18 September read:

1 May	7 cwt at £11/cwt	Purchase price	£77
18 September	9½ cwt at £10·50/cwt	Fat price	£99·75
"Feeder's margin"			£22·75
Food cost	20 weeks' grazing at 50p/week		£10
To cover all other costs and profit			£12·75

Finally store cattle which are bought in spring should preferably have been outwintered rather than housed. The advice to the buyer is "look for mud, not muck, on the coat". This point is mainly of academic interest in the north where weather conditions largely preclude outwintering, but is of some significance in areas which enjoy milder winter weather. The animal which is housed over winter and is sold in spring nearly always suffers an abrupt change in diet and environment because it moves directly from winter quarters and diet to market and directly on to grass. The result of such treatment is that the animal loses up to 1 cwt in liveweight, i.e. of the liveweight purchased, and some 2–4 weeks pass before this is regained. The store which has been outwintered does not suffer the same loss because it does not endure any abrupt change and consequently tends to reach market condition about 2 weeks earlier than the housed store. The outwintered store therefore achieves a greater increase in liveweight during the grazing period and realises a better price when sold because the fat price falls from May to September.

REARING WEANED CALVES

Many weaned calves are reared on during their first winter either because they are too small to achieve slaughter weight and condition before spring or because it is farm policy to rear bigger animals on for fattening on grass. In both situations there is considerable controversy concerning optimum feeding level and rate of liveweight gain during the winter period. One school of thought which includes many farmers argues that the feeding level should be moderate, resulting in a low total winter feed cost, a liveweight gain of about 1 lb daily and consequently, it is said, a big liveweight gain during the subsequent grazing period when feed costs are low. A typical winter ration used when this practice is followed, with animals weighing 400 lb in the autumn, is 30 lb grass silage + 2 lb rising to 3 lb barley grain. It is claimed that while more liberal feeding will result in an increase in the liveweight gain made during the winter, the animals will be in forward condition when turned out to graze and will therefore suffer a severe check. Furthermore, if the animals are sold in spring it is said that many buyers will not bid freely if the animals are in forward condition, again claiming that they will melt away when put out to graze.

These arguments ignore the advantages which follow more liberal feeding, some of which are set out in Table 9.1. (See page 82.) It is assumed that weaned calves of 400 lb liveweight are fed to gain either 1 lb or 2 lb daily throughout a 180-day winter period, and that grass silage (S.E. 10) costed at £3 per ton and barley (S.E. 71.4) at £20 per ton are available.

The advantages are clearly in favour of feeding at the higher level, this resulting in a reduced food cost per lb liveweight gain and a handsome increase in the margin above feed cost plus purchase price. This is so because the cost of the feed required daily by the animal for maintenance is spread over 2 lb liveweight gain, whereas at the lower

TABLE 9.1
WEANED CALVES 400 LB LIVEWEIGHT. MARGIN ABOVE FEED AND PURCHASE PRICE OVER 180-DAY WINTER

	Fed to gain 1 lb/day at 400 lb	at 580 lb		Fed to gain 2 lb/day at 400 lb	at 760 lb
Silage (lb)	30	40		30	50
Barley (lb)	2	2		5	6
Total feed and cost					
Silage	56·25 cwt:	£8·44		64·28 cwt:	£9·64
Barley	3·21 cwt:	£3·21		8·84 cwt:	£8·84
		£11·65			£18·48
400 lb l'wt at £10/cwt (A)		£35·71			£35·71
580 lb l'wt at £12/cwt (B)		£62·14	760 lb l'wt at £12/cwt		£81·43
Feeder's margin (B−A)		£26·43			£45·71
Margin over feed+purchase		£14·78			£27·23
Food cost/lb l'wt gain		6·5p			5·1p
			760 lb l'wt at £11/cwt		£74·64
			Feeder's margin		£38·93
			Margin over feed+ purchase		£20·45

feeding level this maintenance cost must be borne by only 1 lb liveweight gain.

Animals which are liberally fed will be in forward condition in spring and the advantages gained may be reduced unless the diet is changed slowly and gradual turnout is practised. Grass silage should therefore be fed to appetite for the last 3 weeks before turnout while the daily ration of barley is gradually reduced and is held at 2 or 3 lb daily during the last week inside and continued at this level for 2–3 weeks of the grazing period.

The animal which is liberally fed over winter shows to further advantage during the subsequent grazing period. Assuming 2 lb daily liveweight gain, the animal turned out at 760 lb liveweight will be ready to market at about 880 lb liveweight in early July before the seasonal price fall occurs. On the other hand, cattle wintered to gain 1 lb daily and turning out at 580 lb liveweight will not achieve 880 lb liveweight until the end of September when fat prices are low.

The advantage is also clearly in favour of liberal feeding during winter in the case where the animals are sold in spring. Reference to Table 9.1 shows that the margin over feed plus purchase price at

£20·45 is superior even in the event that buyers bid £1 less per live cwt for forward stores.

There is therefore a strong case for the liberal winter feeding of weaned calves which are to be fattened on grass and this practice is recommended.

WINTER FATTENING

The factors affecting the development of a successful winter fattening enterprise have already been discussed separately in earlier chapters, but may conveniently be briefly summarised here. The basic requirements are for the purchase of store cattle at an appropriate price, the production and use of low cost feeds, good stockmanship and sale for slaughter as soon as the animal carries sufficient finish to ensure satisfactory grading.

When cattle are purchased note must be taken of anticipated fat price level and every effort be made to buy at a lower price per live hundredweight and reference should be made to the points to be considered when buying store cattle as discussed on pp. 79–81. The majority of cattle which are fattened in winter are now loose housed in courts and the number per pen should, if possible, be no more than ten or twelve. Even matching of animals is essential and becomes more important as the number per pen increases. Any animal which is being bullied should be withdrawn to an individual pen and the obvious "poor doer" should be sold quickly before heavy feed costs are incurred.

The basic ration of farm produced forages is determined and the amount of additional feed is assessed using the Unit Cost approach discussed on pp. 15–18. Particular care must be taken to avoid the purchase of expensive protein which is not required.

Finally, animals should be slaughtered as soon as they will grade satisfactorily because further feeding only leads to an unprofitable increase in the food cost per pound of liveweight gained and may result in the downgrading of the carcase if it carries excessive fat.

FATTENING ON GRASS

The fattening of cattle on grass is the oldest established method of bringing cattle to slaughter condition and must have been practised in the earliest days of beef production. In spite of this long history, however, this facet of beef production even now offers great scope for improvement in terms of output per acre. This is because traditional forms of grazing management are still widely practised. It would appear that graziers have been loath to adopt more intensive systems of management possibly because it has been accepted that priority should be given to crop enterprises on the farm during the summer growing season.

Given sensible buying of store cattle, the financial return per animal fattened on grass under a traditional grazing system can be quite satisfactory, but the return per acre of grass involved is low when compared with that which can be obtained from arable crops. More intensive grazing systems have been practised for many years by dairy farmers, and many beef producers are now adopting these methods of increasing output per acre.

An increased production of grass can readily be achieved by the more liberal use of fertiliser, particularly nitrogen, but the conversion of the additional grass produced into saleable meat involves an increase in the stocking rate per acre. However, it is difficult to achieve the important objective of offering the grazing animal short, leafy grass throughout the grazing season while practising set stocking at a high rate and some form of rotational grazing becomes essential.

A simple rotational paddock grazing system for younger stock has been described on pp. 61–62. The same system works equally well with older fattening cattle. "Strip grazing", which involves offering the cattle a new area of grass each day in paddocks which are grazed in rotation, is not widely practised with beef cattle. This method can give excellent results, but absolute regularity of timing of the daily movement of the fence is essential. The cattle then quickly adopt a set feeding routine. On many farms, however, priority is given to other field work in summer and fence movement degenerates into an irregular practice and at the worst may occasionally be completely overlooked. The cattle then become unsettled and individual performance suffers although output in terms of liveweight gain per acre may still be at a higher level as compared with set stocking.

The adoption of a simple rotational grazing system avoids the daily chore of fence movement. The inspection of cattle daily is still required, but this can be done when time is available and the cattle only require to be moved once every 3–5 days. Either temporary leys or permanent pastures may be used. Permanent pastures may be a little later in coming into full production in spring but have the advantage of being more resistant at one extreme of weather to drought and at another to poaching. Nitrogen is applied at the rate of 250 units per acre over the season consisting of an initial dressing at the rate of 80 units and subsequently 40 units per acre after each paddock is grazed. The stocking rate required is between two and three animals per acre depending on the liveweight of the available cattle and should result in an initial stocking weight of 1500 to 1700 lb which should rise to 2300 to 2500 lb per acre towards the end of the fattening period. In other words, the liveweight gain per acre should be about 800 lb and the liveweight gain per head will depend on stocking rate being about 266 lb and 320 lb per acre at three and two and a half animals per acre respectively.

The level of nitrogen application may be and often is raised to 300 to 350 units per acre, but it cannot be too strongly emphasised that it is wasteful to produce extra grass unless it can be utilised. It is usually necessary to cut one or two paddocks for ensiling even when 250 units of nitrogen are used. If higher levels are used, either the stocking rate must be raised or more surplus grass must be ensiled or both are required. This calls for very skilled management and a gradual increase in level of manuring to about 250 units of nitrogen per acre is therefore suggested.

The feeding of supplements to older cattle which are being fattened on grass must not be practised simply as a routine and without careful consideration. There is usually a strong case for feeding 2 to 3 lb grain daily for some 2–3 weeks at the beginning of the grazing season to alleviate the abruptness in change of diet and to act as a carrier of calcined magnesite. After this period the feeding of a supplement is unnecessary and indeed wasteful unless drought retards the rate of sward recovery. All the evidence available indicates that, provided short, leafy grass is available, the feeding of a supplement simply depresses grass intake. Subsequently individual animal performance is depressed unless the supplement used is of the same nutritive value as the grass which it replaces. For example, if traditional advice is followed and the animal is offered and eats 3 lb undecorticated cotton cake, this will provide 1·2 lb Starch Equivalent, but this will replace about 3 lb grass dry matter which provides 2·1 lb Starch Equivalent. This depression in Starch Equivalent intake would in turn depress daily liveweight gain by about 0·3 lb. Supplementary feeding must therefore only be practised if and when grass supplies fail and the feed used should be that which offers the cheapest Starch Equivalent unit because the animal's requirement for protein will almost certainly be met by the supplement and the grass which is available.

The results of surveys of commercial grass fattening enterprises appear at first sight to contradict the above advice in that they show that cattle receiving supplementary feed gain 0·2 lb daily more than animals which receive no supplement. Experience indicates, however, that this response is usually a reflection of inferior grazing management. The adoption of a rotational grazing system should reduce the need to use supplements to the odd occasion and lead to an increase in output per acre from the 400 lb liveweight gain obtained on average when traditional grazing systems are practised to 800 lb per acre.

FURTHER READING

REFERENCE has been freely made in this text to various Beef Recording Association (B.R.A.) and Meat and Livestock Commission (M.L.C.) surveys. Students are advised to refer to these and the other publications listed below:

1. Technical Reports Nos. 1–10 B.R.A. (UK) Ltd.
2. Technical Reports, Records Reports and Newsletters published by M.L.C. Beef Improvement Service.
3. An intensive system of beef production from grassland using autumn born calves from the dairy herd. *Joint Beef Production Committee Handbook No. 1*. Published M.L.C. PO Box 44, Queensway House, Queensway, Bletchley, Bucks.
4. The intensive cereal beef system using calves from the dairy herd. *Joint Beef Production Committee Handbook No. 2* (published as No. 3 above).
5. Three systems for beef. *Profitable Enterprise Booklet No. 2*. M.A.F.F. (Publications), Government Buildings, Tolcarne Drive, Pinner, Middlesex.

INDEX